STAR CHILDREN

STAR CHILDREN

Clara Asscher-Pinkhof

Translated by Terese Edelstein and Inez Smidt

Wayne State University Press, Detroit, 1986

Library of Congress Cataloging-in-Publication Data

Asscher-Pinkhof, Clara.
  Star children.

  Translation of: Sterrekinderen.
  1. World War, 1939–1945––Fiction. 2. Jews––
Netherlands––Fiction. I. Title.
PT5807.A78S813   1986   839.3'1364   86-24543
ISBN 0-8143-1846-0
ISBN 0-8143-1847-9 (pbk.)

Photographs courtesy Rijksinstituut voor
Oorlogsdocumentatie–Netherlands State Institute
for War Documentation, Amsterdam.

Grateful acknowledgment is made to the Morris
and Emma Schaver Publication Fund for Jewish
Studies for financial assistance in the publication of
this volume.

To you I dedicate this book,
little star boy,
you who played the harmonica
in hell

Contents

2. Star House

3. Star Desert

4. Star Hell

Foreword

by *Harry James Cargas*

CHILDREN AND DEATH. Those words form one of the great oxymorons of World War II. Almost one million Jewish children were murdered by Nazis and their collaborators before reaching their teens.

What was it like to be a child in a world where you were hated—hated for the crime of having been born? You are about to find out by reading this book—a volume which itself is an oxymoron in a way: a beautiful book about tragedy.

We live in a world of symbols. One way of distinguishing humans from other animals is to say that we are symbol-making creatures. Among the most enduring of such signs are stars, which have been used to stand for eternity, timeless love, hope, great distances, mystery, illusion, and many other things. The Star of David is a symbol of Judaism and as such is a figure of honor. But the Nazis forced Jews to wear yellow stars as badges of shame, as marks of death.

In Jewish scripture there is the story of an angel daubing certain houses to indicate to the Messenger of Death that it was to "pass over" those who lived in these dwellings. So the Nazis marked Jewish men and women, boys and girls, with a sign that indicated to *their* demons of death that those who bore the emblem were to be destroyed.

And indeed many of them were destroyed.

Some have left their stories for us. Anne Frank of the Netherlands was one. Dawid Rubinowicz was another. In their diaries they shared their fears and hopes, their frustrations and their joys. But there is another way to tell what happened to children during the Holocaust, and that is in fiction. While histories, autobiographies, biographies, diaries, journals, psychological and sociological analyses, and other kinds of books can give us statistics, eyewitness accounts, and expert interpretations, fiction has its own truth. The best work universalizes experience for all of us to share in varying degrees according to our abilities, our sensibilities, and, of course, the skills of the writer.

It may move us to a certain degree to learn that perhaps eleven million people were massacred in concentration camps, half of them murdered only because they were Jews. But the "story" of victims in novels like André Schwarz-Bart's *The Last of the Just* and Arnost Lustig's *Night and Hope* and the shorter works of Jakov Lind or Tadeusz Borowski has a far greater impact on most readers than a recital of facts, however horrible. In *Star Children* Clara Asscher-Pinkhof provides us with the profound truth of fiction. She reaches the epitome of effect which Joseph Conrad demanded of the novelist: she makes us think, she makes us feel, but, most of all, she makes us see.

The writer who would be a witness to the Holocaust must beware of a double danger. There is the Scylla of saying too little—of failing to honor the dead through a betrayal by silence and betraying the living, too, by not giving us the story in its full magnitude, in passing it off as just another tragedy, comparable, perhaps, to an earthquake or other unpreventable disasters. The writer must also steer clear of the Charybdis of saying too much, for an undisciplined outpouring, in the face of the horror of the Holocaust, dishonors the dead and the craft of fiction as well. *Star Children* is an excellent example of what literary critics describe as the harmony of content and form. Asscher-Pinkhof gives us a near-perfect amalgam of delicacy of story and integrity of language, not an easy achievement.

In a book which we wrote together some years ago, Élie Wiesel told of coming to realize why he and several other Holocaust survivors wrote in such short, clipped sentences: we didn't know, he said, when we began a sentence, whether we would be alive to finish it, so every word had to contain as much truth as possible. I find this kind of intensity and integrity in Asscher-Pinkhof's fiction. She does honor to her subject, to her readers, to her profession of writing, and to herself by the implosive approach of her novel. Each word, each sentence, each image carries the burden of the Holocaust.

This unusual book presents an unusual situation. The experiences here portrayed are not typical of what happened to Jews in other areas under the domination of the Nazis. (This is true also, to a degree, of Belgium and parts of France.) We read here of prisoners being allowed to keep thermos bottles through two camps, and even of getting them filled on Sundays; of being permitted to keep with them Purim scrolls, suitcases, tablecloths, toys, attractive dresses, etc. Family visits were occasionally sanctioned. Perhaps most startling, when compared to the treatment of Jews in Eastern Europe, is that children were kept alive for a time, remaining with their mothers, and that even the elderly were not immediately selected for the gas chambers.

But we must not be deceived. The overall Dutch tragedy was enormous: only 20,000 Dutch Jews survived World War II; 105,000 perished. Add to this the total of 30,000 to 40,000 Jewish refugees who fled to Holland from other countries and who were also murdered there, and we get some sense of that dark period.

Jewish people had lived in the Netherlands for centuries. They did not live in ghettos and were fully integrated citizens of their nation. Their non-Jewish countrymen actively helped them to evade Nazi measures against them, and many thousands of Dutch people lost their lives in that effort, but it was an unequal fight. After the Jews in Amsterdam put up a valiant resistance, the Germans crushed them brutally. Holland is a flat country with few forests outside of the marshlands, no places to hide. It is also very small, bordered by the enemy, Germany, on the east, occupied Belgium to the south, and the sea to the north and west. Once the Nazi juggernaut gained momentum, the fate of the Jews was not in doubt. (This, incidentally, in spite of an imaginative delaying tactic by some Dutch resistance groups, which tried to prove that a relatively large number of Jews were not "racially" Jews at all, using what Nora Levin describes as historical and anthropological "quasi-scientific memoranda," an argument which the German officials actually accepted for a brief period in 1942—certainly one of the more creative efforts on behalf of Jews during the war.)

The impact of the Holocaust is now a part of our heritage. To deny it or to ignore it in any way would signify our personal and collective unwillingness to assume a responsibility to try to know where possible, to try to repent where appropriate, to try to prevent where necessary. Our gratitude, then, must be expressed to Clara Asscher-Pinkhof, to the translators, for their self-imposed task of sharing her words with us, and to the publisher's staff for telling this story to a new generation of readers.

Preface

OUR INVOLVEMENT WITH *Star Children* began in the winter of 1984 when Inez checked the book out of the public library in Leiden. We both read the book and were overwhelmed not only by the stories the author tells but also by the subtleties and extreme sensitivity and beauty of her writing. When we went to a bookstore to buy copies of it to send to family, we were informed that *Star Children* had never been translated into English. Together we worked on several chapters and sent it to the publisher with a letter inquiring about the possibility of translating the entire book. The publisher wrote back that while the firm could not be responsible for having the book translated, it would be very pleased if we were to find an American publisher interested in issuing an edition of *Sterrekinderen* in English. The two of us worked a little more on the book, but then Terese moved back to the States, and the translation was put aside for awhile. In April 1985, we showed our translation to Harry Cargas, who encouraged us to pursue the possibility, and so we did.

Work on the project was undertaken with the attitude that we were the translators, not the authors, and that this is Clara Asscher-Pinkhof's book, not ours. Accordingly, we have tried to adhere as closely as possible to the Dutch text. Of course, even with this conservative approach it was necessary to rework a great deal of the original book in order to put it into acceptable English. It was also important for us to keep in mind that most of the sketches were written from a child's point of view, and this accounts for the simple word choice, the straightforward style, and the references to horrors in naive and innocent terms (for example, the SS are called "the men in green" and Kristallnacht the "terrible night in Germany").

Inez Smidt is a Dutch physician who lives in Leiden. Terese Edelstein is an American who lived in Leiden from 1980 to 1984.

T.E.
I.S.

About the Author

CLARA ASSCHER-PINKHOF was born on October 25, 1896, in Amsterdam, the fourth in a family of eight children. Her father was a physician, author of medical works, editor of a medical journal (*Tijdschrift voor Geneeskunde*), a scholar of Judaism, and a Zionist leader. In spite of his many responsibilities he personally instructed his children in Jewish history, in the study of the Bible, and in Hebrew. Clara's mother was a piano teacher, and Clara became a teacher as well. Her early contact with children led toward Clara's first children's stories and poems, which appeared initially in children's magazines and later in book form.

In 1919, she married Avraham Asscher, who became chief rabbi in the city of Groningen. During the short course of their marriage, six children were born, the youngest of whom was four months old when Avraham died in 1926.

In order to support her large family Clara gave readings, taught university-level courses, and continued to write children's books. Her first novel, *De weg alleen* (The Way Alone), appeared in 1935. Three more novels followed from 1936 to 1939, during which time she also translated English children's books into Dutch.

Like the lives of all Dutch Jews, Clara's own life

changed drastically after the Germans overran Holland in 1940. Because Jewish children were no longer allowed to attend school with non-Jews, special schools had to be established. Due to an acute shortage of teachers for the Jewish schools, Clara returned to Amsterdam and rejoined the profession. She continued to instruct until she was deported in May 1943. She also served as a volunteer assistant in the "Hollandse Schouwburg," a theater that the SS had turned into a kind of detention center. This is the "Star House" of her book, and it was here that the Jews of Amsterdam were taken after they had been caught in a roundup. They were usually held in the theater for about twenty-four hours, until they were put into trams and taken to the train station. From there they were sent to one of the transit camps in Holland.

The idea for *Star Children* came to Clara very suddenly. She began writing about the events under the Hitler regime as seen through the eyes of the children who were marked with a yellow star.

New Year's morning, 1943. I awoke from a deep sleep, and on my lips were the words "Star Children."

Star Children. The children with the Jewish star. They went past me, the star children that I had known and knew in the critical times in the city and in the theater that was their prison. The dead children and the living. I knew at that moment that I had to be their voice—that I had to speak out and say what they had felt and suffered— what they were still feeling and suffering. I saw the little boy who had put his harmonica, an indispensable item, into his rucksack, and who played his songs for me amid the frenzy in the theater. I knew that *Star Children* would be dedicated to him because he stood at the head of the long, endless line of star children for whom a thin, barely audible little song was more important than all that was happening around them and to them. [*]

---

[*]Clara Asscher-Pinkhof, *Danseres zonder Benen* (Dancer without Legs) (Uitgeverij Leopold, 1966), p. 169.

Clara wrote the first two parts of the book while living in the ghetto of Amsterdam ("Star City"). When she felt that the time for her own deportation was approaching, she entrusted the manuscript to her publisher, promising him that if she survived the war, she would finish the work.

Clara was sent first to Westerbork ("Star Desert"), a camp in the province of Drenthe, near the German border, where she continued her work with children by helping in the girls' dormitory and in the nursery in the children's barrack. It was in Westerbork that her relationship with Mindel Fuld began. Mindel, the little girl bound for Palestine in the fourth part of this book, was a baby when her parents fled to Palestine, leaving her behind in Holland. She was placed in a Jewish orphanage, which was subsequently "emptied" by the Nazis, and was four years old when the author found her in the nursery at Westerbork.

Clara had been granted a Palestine "certificate" or entrance permit by the Red Cross because her daughter Roza had gone to Palestine to live in 1939. Upon learning about Mindel's background, she arranged to have the child's name included on her certificate in the hope of being able to return the little girl to her parents. Although the German authorities assured her that she would be permitted to stay at Westerbork and take care of Mindel there, Clara chose to go to Bergen-Belsen, which at that time was thought to be a camp for exchange prisoners.

Thus instead of remaining behind in Holland (and eventually being deported to one of the death camps in Poland), Clara and Mindel were sent to Bergen-Belsen, the "Star Hell" of this book. In July 1944, about three hundred inmates were suddenly exchanged for German prisoners. Although Clara did not originally belong to this select group, she was added to it one-half hour before its departure. She was sent to Palestine, where she was able to see Mindel and her parents reunited and where she resumed her writing of the book:

The typewriter stood on an orange crate and need be returned to its generous owner only when I had finished my book *Star Children.* For the star children were rising up in me again, and they wanted me to write down what they were dictating to me.

They dictated day and night. They had done that in the camps, too, when I could not write it down. There was no more postponing it now. It lay ready in me, word for word, and I had only to listen and to type. It exhausted me and made me happy at the same time.*

Clara finished *Star Children* one week before the liberation of Holland, and as soon as the postal service between Palestine and Holland was renewed, she sent the manuscript to her publisher as she had promised. The book was published by Uitgeverij Leopold in 1946 and is now in its ninth printing in Holland. A perennial favorite, *Star Children* has been translated into Danish, Swedish, Serbo-Croatian, Hebrew, and German; it received the Jugendbuchpreis in Germany in 1962. It appears here in English for the first time.

---

*Ibid., p. 276.

STAR CHILDREN

1. Star City

Star Dance

THERE HAS BEEN a roundup today.

Already in the early morning the dim rumor had blown over to this street of Jews: they were busy in other neighborhoods, and soon they would come here, too. They were standing in little groups in the street, the men and women, their eyes full of bewilderment and their voices shrill from tension. They did not know where it was better: in the house where they could trample down the door and drag you from the stairs, or in the street where they could take you in passing and push you into the police van. Oh, in the street you had each other, with all your despair but with all your sense of togetherness, and you could always go inside as soon as you saw the van and uniforms entering the street.

The threat was the worst. It hung heavily over the street in the warm summer air, paralyzing, suffocating. A little old woman, her shopping bag over her arm, had gone out when she had not yet known of the roundup. But then she could not find her way home because it had suddenly grown from half a street to an endless road of terror. She grasped a large woman whom she did not know and cried, "I can't go alone! I can't go alone!" The woman supported her and soothed her, just as you soothe a child. The little woman wailed softly, "But I haven't done anything! But I haven't done anything!"

No one had done anything, the men and women who were standing in little groups, and the star children, who were being chased inside by the shrieking voices of their mothers. The children had to be inside, God save them! What would they do in the street if the violence came closer and closer?

And then it *was* there, sudden and terrible. All at once the streets were empty. The men in green invaded the houses and hauled people away. Some were silent and defeated, some were protesting, others were crying miserably. They were hauled away, until the hunger for Jews was satiated and the human prey was carried off.

Slowly, slowly the people appeared again, to see each other, to look for each other. To count, to know what was left.

The mothers no longer kept the children inside—if they were still there. They were thinking about things quite different than the care of the children—about the father who was taken, about the other street where dear ones lived, about the terror that still seemed to fill the small, stuffy room. Oh, no, the children had free play.

There has been a roundup today.

The women are leaning out over the window sills and are calling out their experiences of today into the summer evening. The men and women are standing on the pavement below; they may still do that, for it is not yet eight o'clock. From upstairs to downstairs and from downstairs to upstairs, the air is full of voices—enumerations of who was taken away. It is a dismal census, a dark review of arms.

But in the middle of the street the star children have formed a circle. Seriously and full of abandonment they are singing their dance song. Those of the small inner ring are the rulers; they have to choose and give out turns.

Those of the outer circle wish to be chosen, and they thrust out their little stomachs or star-covered chests. There is nothing in the world that is important anymore, only if you are chosen and may dance in that small ring.

> Choose someone now,
> Choose someone now,
> Whom you like the best,
> And then go dance with him!
> Tralalalalalala,
> Tralalalalalala,
> That's it, now it is over,
> And others will be coming!

The men and women leaning out of the windows, two and three stories high, and those on the pavement below are talking, calling, complaining, asking. They neither see nor hear the circle there in the middle of the street.

The star children are singing, dancing, choosing, recruiting. They neither hear nor see the sorrow that is rebounding from upstairs to downstairs, from downstairs to upstairs.

> Tralalalalalala,
> Tralalalalalala,
> That's it, now it is over . . .

But no others will be coming. For the fathers and mothers, the big brothers and sisters have been taken away, and no others will be coming in their places.

The eyes of those who wish to be chosen are beaming at the choosers, and the air of the summer evening in the narrow street is full of children's song.

Merry Child

LIFE IS A celebration, and each day brings new, exciting adventures. The experience of her six years has taught her so; no worried adult faces, no subdued, oldish child's talk can take that away from her. Whoever looks at her has a friendly look—thus everyone is out to heighten her enjoyment. The things that happen are merry changes from her usual schedule; thus the things happen to increase her joy. That's right, isn't it?

And now there has come about something marvelous and new: a star on her coat, a star on her cardigan, a star on her summer dress, even a star on her school pinafore! Never before has she had anything like this, and her little sister does not even have it because she is not yet six years old. But she—just as father has it on his coat and mother has it on her dress and coat—she has it, too: an orange star with "Jew" on it. Tomorrow she may go along the street with that, and to school. Everyone will look at her and know that she is six years old, and a Jew. Everyone will nod to her and wink, even more than usual, and she will share a little secret with everyone: that she is six years old and a Jew.

It is a pity that all the other children at the primary school are six years old. It will not be at all unusual to come to school with a star. But because it is new, when they arrive at school they will all look at each other's dress or coat, and perhaps some or all of the other mothers might have forgotten to sew a star on the school pinafore, and then she will be the only one in the class who sits upright and proper at her desk, with a star on her pinafore.

And Jukie? Will Jukie's mother have thought of the star? Tomorrow she will call for Jukie even earlier than usual, and if she comes out of the house without a star, she will look at Jukie with her hand over her mouth, shocked, and say, "Oh, you don't have any star on! That's not allowed!" And then Jukie will go quickly inside to ask her mother for a star, and perhaps they will be late for school, but they will not be punished because that star, they must wear it, musn't they?

She has gone out the door, radiant and full of hope. She has almost convinced her mother that it actually is a celebration. Mother watched her dancing along the street. When mother went inside, she had a small and very humble prayer in her heart: please that it might remain a celebration, or that she might continue dancing with the star on her coat.

And now she comes home from school; the feet are dancing, the eyes are happy, but the mouth is set in a serious and obligatory pucker.

"Was it nice?" asks mother. The daily question.

"Oh, very nice!" The daily answer.

And then the one swiftly follows the other, the serious pucker is accidentally lost in her hurry to tell it all.

"It was so nice with the star. And all the people said hello to me. And Jukie's mother had remembered it, too, and almost all the mothers, but a few had forgotten it, and that's not allowed! Mother, is that all right, to go without a star?"

She does not wait for the answer, but suddenly remembers the serious pucker. Her little mouth contracts, and her eyes become covered by a sorrowful haze.

"But it's not entirely nice, that star. It is also *very* bad. Right, mother?"

"Why?" asks mother, interested.

She sighs.

"Jukie says so."

"Oh," says mother. "And why?"

She sighs again.

"Jukie didn't say why," she confesses, embarrassed.

Breakdown

THE SUN SHINES burning hot in all the neighborhoods of the city—thus in all the Jewish quarters of the city, too. It really is a pity that those Jewish quarters are so far apart and that the streets in between have no shade.

The sunshine reaches far into their little kitchen and back room. They live rather close to the sun, anyway, much closer than the people who live on the first and second floors. In the winter they lived close to the cold and wind and especially close to the rain, for that came inside as a matter of course, like a good neighbor. Then they had liked it when the sun shone inside for a while. But now that the sun is constantly coming inside for the whole day, they have long since ceased to enjoy it.

Mother must wait in line this morning. They do not know why exactly. They do not know if it is to learn something about father, or to get some vegetables, or both, but mother has not told them. And an errand must be run in another Jewish quarter, far away. They must go there, then; the eight-year-old brother and six-year-old sister can very well take their litttle two-year-old sister along with them.

They cried a bit at first because they did not want to take her. The little girl is too heavy for them to carry. And for her to walk, so far? She cannot even walk to the end of the street.

Mother scolded such as she never did before father went away, and such as she so often does now. She surely cannot leave the child alone in the house? And she cannot let the child stand in line, or carry her all those hours?

The oldest child shouted that he could not carry her, either, and that he had to go much farther than mother. And then mother suddenly became kind again, and she promised him a wagon that he could use to pull his little sister. The people below have a little wagon that they have made themselves from a margarine crate and two sets of wheels. They will gladly lend that to the children.

And now together they pull their neighbors' wagon along the burning-hot streets. Their little sister sits on a thin cushion inside it. She whines a little because she is so warm and because she is being jostled so. The two older ones are not paying any attention; it is difficult enough for them to lift the wagon up and down from the sidewalks. If they should say something to her, she would only begin to cry even harder.

Their hands pulling the feathery rope of the wagon are wet with sweat. Their necks, their hair, their whole faces and bodies are wet. Oh, and their feet are hurting in their thin, worn-out shoes that have long since been irreparable.

The wagon has fallen lopsided upon the wheels a few times. They have let their little sister step out so that she would be quiet and forget to whine and so that they could shove the wagon back to the middle of the sets of wheels. But because he is the oldest, the brother has seen that after a while it will go completely off the wheels and that the bottom will break through, too. His throat is pinched tight with fear because they are just at the beginning of the other Jewish quarter; they must still run the errand in the middle of that neighborhood and then go the whole way back. How will they do that?

When they have finished the errand and are just about to begin the way back, it happens: the bottom cracks, the little girl screams, the one wheel comes off of the axle. The little one did not hurt herself, for the margarine crate was quite close to the ground. But all three of them are so frightened, and they are so far from home!

The brother walks up to a man who is passing by. He is not wearing a star. Perhaps he can help them.

"My little sister's wagon is in pieces and we have so far to go."

The man looks at the hopeless little wagon and says,

"You had better go back in the tram. Have you money with you for the tram?"

"We aren't allowed in the tram," says the boy, resigned, "because we're Jews."

"Oh, yes," says the man. "Then I don't know."

The little boy goes back to his two sisters and the broken wagon. He will now ask someone with a star because such a person will be more understanding about not being allowed to take the tram.

He pulls on the sleeve of a young woman.

"My little sister's wagon is in pieces and we have so far to go."

When she sees the little girl and the wagon, she fortunately says nothing about a tram. She only looks about to see if she can bring help from somewhere. Suddenly she walks away, for there is a man riding by on a carrier cycle, a man without a star. She talks with him and points to the three children and the little wagon. At first the man shakes his head, and in the distance the oldest nearly cries with fear. But then the man nods and they both approach them.

"Step in," says the man to the two oldest. He takes the wheels, the margarine crate, and the little girl all at the same time and loads them onto his carrier cycle.

The children climb over the fender and onto the cycle.

"Where do you live?" asks the man.

The boy tells him.

"Come on, let's go."

The three of them and the remains of the wagon have plenty of room in the empty carrier cycle.

The Jewish quarter is hot, and the streets leading to the other Jewish quarter have no shade, but the little sister is no longer whining and their hands are no longer sweating. They are being driven—just like that—even more quickly and more easily than going by tram.

It is a pity, a pity that their Jewish quarter is not even farther away. For it is wonderful to be driven.

First Worry

A GROUP OF little boys is playing at the end of the Jewish street. A yellow board is standing there that states, at least, where the Jewish street ends or begins, where star children and children without stars live next to and above and below each other. Some of those playing are star boys, others are not; they cannot tell the difference very well because they have not been born with or without a star and because their mothers have sewn the stars on their shirts, and not they themselves. And since they played with each other before the stars existed, why should they not continue to do so?

They are playing enthusiastically and with abandonment. If they agree with each other, they chuckle and use the strong words that they have heard the fathers without stars using. If they disagree with each other, they scold and scream, just as they have heard the star mothers doing. For in their fear and unceasing anxiety the star mothers have no possibility of expression other than in their cry of despair, which takes form in reproaching and threatening those who are dearest to them. And who is more dear to those little boys than their friends? Thus they have to yell at those friends, haven't they?

The patched or sometimes no longer patched trousers are hanging around their thin legs. Their trousers are baggy and too long as well. But when the boys squat in the midst of their enthusiasm, the trousers suddenly stretch and mercilessly reveal the patches or holes. But the boys are not aware of the appearance of their trousers and of the rest of their clothing. They have other things on their minds!

Evening is falling, and soon it will be time for the star boys to go inside. The others, then, will not be staying outside any longer, either. It will be no fun if half of the group is gone.

In the twilight their clothes seem less shabby, their

hands, legs, and faces less thin. There is shadow every-where, and it is into this shadow that their oldish features fade away. But their faces have not yet become carefree, not even in the semidarkness.

High above their heads in the taut pale sky, a small row of airplanes is looming. The planes are so high that they are barely visible, but their roar is clear and piercing. The passersby are standing still and gazing in surprise, their eyes squinting and peering.

The boys are also watching. They stop whatever they are playing, get up from their squatting positions, and look at the sky. They are pointing out to each other and voicing their opinions about the source and target of the planes, and shouting their scorn and indignation for those they believe to be wrong. Then suddenly it occurs to one of the star boys what can happen if such airplanes go high over your head. He turns his oldish face away from the sky toward his friends without stars and scolds in the voice of his mother and of so many of the mothers from the street, "For God's sake go inside, for if you get your heads cracked open, then we've done it again!"

Return

WHEN THE MEN came to get them, very late in the evening, father and mother awakened her. She was very sleepy and did not really understand what was going to happen to her. Her brothers did. They kept their lips pressed tightly together and spoke only when necessary during the pack-ing. Her brothers were like that; if they thought that some-thing was terrible, then they did not talk about it, like father and mother. But she was just a girl, and the youngest, besides. If she thought that something was terrible, then she had to say so aloud, and sometimes cry as well. If she thought that something was wonderful, then she had to express her happy thoughts aloud, too.

She gradually began to understand that she was going to be taken away by those men. She was so frightened that she could not even cry. She only stood there, motionless. Then mother said very quietly and in a strange, low voice that she must get dressed, and this the little girl did. While she was dressing herself, she noticed that there were many more clothes lying on her chair than she had previously taken off. She nonetheless put on all those clothes until she stood stiff and propped up, like a doll. Then she waited. She did not pack. Father buckled her full, heavy rucksack behind her back, and finally she and the others went out the door with the men, across the dark street to the car where silent adults and crying children were awaiting them.

Inside the car she became a bit more alert. She asked father where the young woman who lived with them was, and father whispered to her that she must not ask about it, and that the woman was all right. The little girl then understood that the woman did not have to go with them.

Then she did not mind everything so much. She looked around and was curious about what would happen next. She pushed the crying of the children and adults out of her thoughts; she told herself that they would presently not cry anymore and not be unhappy anymore, once they had become used to it all, just as she had. In the dark they rode in the tram. It was terribly crowded, with all those rucksacks, but she had not been in a tram for such a long time that she almost enjoyed it. All the things that had been prohibited for such a long time were suddenly permitted—trams, trains, being on the street at night. And tomorrow she would not have to go to school.

Many things happened during those weeks over there. First she became ill, and she felt very awful and nauseated and burning hot. She lay in the strange hospital barrack. When mother came to visit her, she hoped that mother would become ill, too. But mother lived in the large barrack with all those strange women, and although she became thin and pale, she did not become ill.

When she was better, she went back to her mother. Father and her brothers lived in another barrack, for men. But there came a night when mother was called up, and father in the other barrack, too, and many other people as well, and then they went to pack again because all of them had to travel further on. Some of the women wept bitterly because they had to go further on, yet they packed while crying, for they still had to take provisions along for themselves and their children!

Mother did not cry, and she knew for certain that her father and her brothers, who were packing in the other barrack, were not crying, either. She herself did not mind that they had to go further on; whether she was here or further on, she was in any case no longer in her own home, and her own things, her own books, her own friends, and her own class were lost to her.

And then something strange happened: they had finished packing and were just about to leave with all the other people who had been called up, when a message came to mother, that father and mother, her brothers and she herself could climb back into their beds again, for they did not have to go away. And the strangest thing was that she did not know whether she was happy about it or not.

They stayed there, then, for many days, and they went through many nights in which other people who were called up had to pack and go away. Mother had to say goodbye to many women. Usually those women cried, and often they kissed mother and kissed her, too, because she was mother's child and because they thought mother was so nice.

And then the strangest message of all came to them— a message that almost never came to one who was brought here: they could go home, all of them, to their own home.

She did not understand much about it. She knew that the young woman who lived with them in their house had stayed and that it therefore had remained just as it was.

The woman had now and then sent food parcels and therefore they had not suffered that much from hunger. But permission to go home was not due to the woman but to the men at father's work who had written and telephoned to say how necessary father was.

Father told them all this as they were sitting together in the train. They were riding the train just as ordinary, free people did, in the daylight and unguarded. It was like a beautiful story, except she did not quite believe it because the story seemed a bit too beautiful.

And then they walked through the streets of their own city and saw their own people and were greeted and kissed, and she began to believe in the story a little more. Before they came to their own house she was already thinking that tomorrow she would be going to school again, and she wondered which dress she should wear—certainly a dress that had not undergone the journey—and she wondered if she had missed much at school and if it would be difficult to catch up on everything.

And suddenly, by chance, when she came around the corner of a street, she stood opposite her best friend, a girl who sat next to her at school. Both of them stood dead still, and they blushed and did not know what to say.

She was the first to speak. A bit surprised and a bit disappointed, she blurted out, "Oh, you have new glasses on!"

Women's Talk

THEY ARE PLAYING tea set, just as little girls did in mother's time and in grandmother's time, with the bottoms of tiny cups layered thickly with sugar, with grains of sugar spilled all around, and with water in the teapot and cookie crumbs on the saucers. Their manners are lady-like, their voices are ladylike, their conversation is lady-like. Whom have they taken as a model for their affecta-tion, for the positions into which they twist their bodies, for the sweet singing of their voices? Has there ever been a mother who has answered this question? The teapot evokes their actions; the flatness of their little bodies causes them to turn and twist themselves somewhat, to look like visiting ladies; the harmlessness of their talk, since they are merely children, must be transformed into something adultlike as soon as they bring a cup of water to their pursed lips. Oh, they do not need a model.

The older one is receiving, the younger one is visiting. She knocks loudly on the door, and when the older girl has called "come in," the little one enters in a cumbersome manner, decked in a hat from the hatrack and a starred cardigan from her mother. She must adorn herself with borrowed stars because she herself is still too young to have to wear them.

"How are you?" asks the hostess.

"I'm fine!" the guest replies cheerfully.

"You must say: oh, what will become of us."

"Oh, what will become of us," sighs the guest meekly.

"Take your coat off," invites the hostess.

"No, that has my star on, hasn't it?" she says, falling out of her role.

"Keep it on then. Do you take sugar in your tea?"

"A whole lot."

They pour and spill and lick and spoon. The conversa-tion drags a bit but blossoms again when the cups are empty and the fingers sticky.

"How is your husband?" inquires the hostess.

"Oh, what will become of us," remembers the guest.

"No, your husband was in Poland."

"My husband is in Poland."

The older child shakes her head compassionately.

"Has he been away for a long time?"

"Oh, yes, for a long time."

"Have you heard from him?"

The little one hesitates.

"Yes, I've heard from him."

"Oh, no, of course you haven't heard from him."

"I haven't heard from him," she concedes.

"Tt-tt," the hostess shakes her head. "And how are your children?"

The younger girl has to think about it for a while. Then she cheers, triumphantly, "My children are stamped!"*

They are playing tea set, just as little girls did in mother's time and in grandmother's time.

Grandson

GRANDMA IS MADE of porcelain. You hardly dare to shake her hand with your strong boyish grip because you are used to grasping so tightly and grandma's hand would certainly fall into pieces if you did that.

She has not been able to move her legs for years. He has never seen her walk, at least, and he is eleven years old. When he was little, he had asked his mother anxiously several times if grandma's legs were whole, because things that were broken were so dreary to him. Grandma's legs are whole, it is just that she cannot move them. If they had been broken it would not have been as easy to love her so very much as he does now. He *would* have

---

*The child is referring to a "sperr," which was a large black "J" stamped on one's identification papers. The fortunate bearer of such a stamp was free of labor calls until further notice and thus could not be deported.—Translators

loved her, except he would have had to have tried his utmost; but he does not have to do that now.

She lives in a very big house. All the people there are sick or are incapacitated in some way, which is why they live in that house. When he goes to grandma's room, he meets all of those people. He looks the other way, then, but nevertheless he says hello to them because they are nice people and because they cannot help that they are so eerie to look at. He is glad when he comes to grandma and sees her lying so whole and white and clean in her bed. She reaches her thin, white hand out to him and smiles at him with her small, white face. Everything about her is white and smooth and fine. He would like to stroke her if his hands were not so strong and so black. When he is with grandma, he always has the feeling that he should have washed his hands just one more time.

Her voice is just as thin as her hands. She asks him things that no other adult may ask, for then he would rudely say "yes" or "no" and think to himself, "You're asking only because you don't know what else to say to me, but you don't care in the least what I say." But he knows that grandma cares very much—that is the difference. Therefore he explains everything to her in a voice that is much softer than the one he uses outside this room. Then she looks at him with her sweet eyes—the only thing about her that is not white—and she nods when she understands him. He knows for certain that she never nods before she has comprehended it. Therefore he loves to tell her the things that are actually intended for boys and not for white, porcelain grandmas.

Then one Monday morning when he is on his way to school, he comes past the square where grandma's big house is and is held back. He may not go past. He does not find this unusual because there is so much that is no longer allowed. It does not matter if you are late for school when something like this happens; you make a detour because there is nothing else you can do, and you do not run because the schoolmaster does not mind if you come late.

But then he sees the big vans parked in front of grandma's building and suddenly he knows that something very terrible is happening. He walks a few steps to the front but is shoved back. No one may come closer, including himself, even if this horrible thing is going to happen to his own grandma.

People are being carried out of the house and shoved into the vans. Crippled people—people who cannot move their arms or legs—people who must let themselves be carried quietly and shoved and driven away because they cannot do anything else. He cannot see who they are, he can only hear some of them crying very loudly and fearfully. He would like to run away if his legs were not so weak, like grandma's. He knows that grandma will not cry, at least not loudly. He will not hear her voice, and he will not see her face, but one of those being carried out there and shoved into the van is grandma—and he cannot stop it.

When his legs can move again and his head is no longer buzzing and whirling, he penetrates through the crowd of people standing behind him, watching, and with dragging feet walks past the detour to school. He does not care anymore, oh, he does not care about anything anymore. If a bomb falls, he does not care; if he comes home and father and mother have been taken away, he does not care; if the schoolmaster no longer wants him in the class, he does not care; if no one wants him anymore, he does not care—for grandma, who is made of porcelain, has been bound up and shoved into a big van.

He rings the bell of the school and is let inside. He takes his coat off because he does that every day. He knows where to find his classroom because he goes inside there every day.

Each pupil has his language lesson in front of him and is writing quietly.

How strange. How can you just sit there and write your language lesson when your grandma has been shoved into a van? But oh, he does not care.

The schoolmaster says something to him. Perhaps he is asking him something. He has not understood exactly.

Now the schoolmaster asks again, and he understands this time.

"Why are you so late?"

Strange. A strange question.

The teacher asks him again.

Then he speaks, and his voice is loud and hoarse as it goes above the large, quiet class.

"I couldn't get by."

Star Wife

SHE GOES ABOUT with a wedding ring, a star, and an unhappy little face; therefore this child is a star wife.

Why did she marry him, anyway? She really does not know. She asks herself that question during the day when she is working and at night when she is in the solitude of her girlhood room in her parents' house. She has not seen him since he slid the ring on her finger; she does not know where he is and whether she will ever in her life see him again. She does not even know if she would like to see him, for he would certainly be angry with her since she did not follow him when he was sent further on. Father and mother said that she must not follow him. No, she knows for sure that she would rather not see him again, for she is afraid of anyone who is angry with her, and she is certainly afraid of him.

Why did she marry him? Well, he said that he loved her and he kissed her and then, somewhat later, she became engaged to him. They both wore engagement rings, and it was rather pleasant to be engaged. Later they had the banns posted, for everyone did that as quickly as possible in order to be together if something should happen.

She thought that nothing would ever happen to them; nothing ever happened to her in her whole life except that he kissed her and that he was engaged to her and that the banns were posted. All the bad things that happen to other people would never happen to her.

And then just two days before they were to be married, he received his deportation notice. Father and mother said that the marriage must not take place now because she could still remain here in safety. She thought so too, then—as long as she had not talked to him about it. He would naturally feel that it would be better for her to remain here in safety and not to have to go away to who-knows-where. Later, when everything was past and he came back again, they could always be married.

But on the day before they were to be married he came to her and her parents himself. He thought that the ordinary thing for her to do would be to marry him and go away with him. He was angry with father and mother who did not think so, and he was angry with her because she obeyed them. And she could not stand an angry voice and angry words.

Then he spoke to her alone. He became nice to her again and he kissed her, so that she was happy again because the anger was past. And then she noticed that she had said yes, that it was all right with her, and that she would marry him.

She married him the following day. Father and mother and all those who were present wept. It did not not seem like a festive occasion at all. She did not cry, for she thought throughout that something would intervene so that she would not have to go away. It did not seem possible that something bad could happen to her.

He left for the camp an hour after everything was over. She cried a little then, for she was no longer certain whether something would come between them and the bad things. He was sweet to her and kissed her, but he was counting on her to come follow him, and she would rather not think about that because she found it so awful. She merely said yes to everything, and she let him kiss her.

Two days later came his telegram: she should come now, for the day after tomorrow he was to be sent further on. She should bring everything with her, and then they would go on together.

She wept bitterly, for she did not want to go to who-knows-where. Father and mother said that if she did not want to go, she should not go, for then it would never be good. She should not have married him, they said. But he *wanted* to get married—she had no choice, had she? Father and mother let her send a telegram herself, and she sent it, weeping: "Parents won't let me."

That was their last contact. She never received an answer from him.

And now she goes about with a wedding ring, a star, and an unhappy little face—this star wife.

Market Woman

SCHOOL DAYS HAD been a wonderful time for her. All the girls were her friends. She laughed with them and whispered big secrets and worried about tests with them. They shared all the pleasures and all the miseries together. In addition to that there were those high marks that surprised her more than anyone else and the obvious way in which the teachers showed that they considered her to be a top-notch student. Oh, school days had been a wonderful time for her.

And then suddenly something incomprehensible came about: she was no longer allowed to attend school. Before the summer vacation she was promoted with such a good report card that none of the girls could take their eyes off it. They were not jealous at all, for their friendship was too close for that. She received a very complimentary speech from the director, which caused her to blush to the roots of her hair. But she may no longer attend school now. For she is a Jew.

She is the only Jew in her class, and on the first day of school after that letter came she knows exactly how all of them will look at her empty seat. They will say softly that she is not sick but is only Jewish and that is the reason she will not be coming back.

She does not cry that entire first day. She would not even know how to cry when something happens that she does not understand at all. This *cannot* be, to have done nothing wrong and then to be sent away from school! The director also knows that this cannot be, for included with the typed letter in which all the very worst things were written was a letter he added himself—sad words, all, but he could not change the situation.

She does not cry on the second day, either, but reads over her French papers because there is French class during the second hour. When she has sat through that second hour, she sets her French books and papers back in the cabinet and goes to school. She knows that she cannot go in, but she remains waiting at the school door, faithful as a dog.

Someone rings the bell, and when she hears the caretaker shuffling toward the door, she hides away in a niche at the side of the door. The man who has rung the bell goes inside, but she must remain outside, for she is not allowed to come in. And then, because that strange man *is* allowed to enter, her face suddenly becomes wet with the tears that she cannot hold back.

When the man comes out again, her tears have dried. She forgets to hide far enough away, and the caretaker who has let the man out sees her. He merely shakes his head sadly and says nothing. But she does not cry again; she does not cry when other people are around.

The bell rings, and then the others come outside. Busy—ordinary—filled with everything that happens at school. But those from her class see her and are startled.

Suddenly she is afraid that they will ask her why she has come; she will not be able to answer that question because she really does not know. But they do not ask her anything. Two girls slide their arms into both of hers, and they walk home, just as if she had been in school, too.

She asks about their work in French.

"Rotten," they say. "You haven't missed anything."

But she knows that she certainly would have gotten something from the class.

When they go their separate ways, the girls ask if she will come to the school again tomorrow.

"No," she says shortly. She is very certain that she will not. She does not want to flee into the little niche for the caretaker again—she does not want to see a strange man go in again while she herself must remain outside—she does not want to walk with the other girls again as if she had been in school and yet know that she has missed everything.

"What are you going to do?" they ask.

At home they said that there would be another school, just for Jews. But she does not want to go to school anymore, ever again. You cannot be taken away from your friends and your place in the class and from your teachers and from your books, just like that. You cannot just go into a strange building and sit down in a strange place and say, "All right, I'm starting all over again."

"Nothing," she says rudely.

The others think that she is angry with them, but they cannot help that she is no longer allowed to attend school.

"Goodbye," says one of them helplessly.

She does not want to depart on bad terms with her friends and therefore she quickly says, "I don't know what I'm going to do yet. But I'm not going to school—not to any other school, either."

"Of course not." They do their best to understand her. "But something will come up."

She shrugs her shoulders and says goodbye to them.

One calls after her, "Keep your chin up!" and then she has to laugh a little inside because it is just as if they had paid her a sick call.

That afternoon during school time, she sees another Jewish girl from her school. She is older and is in a different class, and they have never had anything to do with each other. But now she suddenly wants to know what that other girl is doing with those dreary, empty days.

"Me?" The girl is actually quite big, for she already has painted lips and permed hair, and she does not look like a schoolgirl at all. "Me? Help a bit in my father's stand at the Jewish market."

She is quiet. That is so *very* different from going to school. And suddenly she knows, too, that this girl did not have painted lips and permed hair at school. She had no time for it then.

"Will you come with me tomorrow?" asks the girl. "You'll be bored otherwise."

She does not want to do anymore French, which is no longer of any use, or geometry, or anything. "All right," she says.

The Jews who buy and the Jews who sell are locked up within a fence. Just like dangerous animals, she thinks, and she almost has to laugh about it.

You may enter only if you have a "J" on your identification card or if they can see by your hair or your eyes or your nose that you are a Jew. But she is not fifteen yet, thus she has no identification card, and her hair is blond. The policeman at the entrance of the gate asks for her identification card, for he does not trust her. She is a bit flattered that he thinks she is fifteen.

"I don't have one," she says, "but I have been sent away from school because I'm a Jew."

That is sufficient for her to be allowed entrance through the gate.

There is calling and shouting and at first she does not know what she is doing here. She looks around with startled eyes and would like very much to go back. But the older girl is going in front of her among the many stands, and she follows meekly.

The girl's father is calling, too. He has lengths of cloth and buttons and shoe laces and ribbons. She takes a good look at him and suddenly remembers that she has seen him behind the counter in a store near them in the neighborhood. Of course that store does not belong to him anymore. Now she finds it pleasant that she has come to help him—at least as long as she does not have to call out.

Sometimes the stand is full of women who are digging up the lengths of cloth and taking everything in their hands and not even buying anything in the end. When they do buy something, she listens with all her attention to how long it takes before they agree about the price. Then she or the other girl wraps the items in a piece of newspaper.

But when the stand is not full and the father is standing and calling for nothing, actually because he has to be doing something, then she listens to what is being shouted from the other stands. Sometimes they make jokes from one stand to the other—nonsense about themselves and about how they are locked up here. You can hardly call it nonsense; it would not be at all strange to look up and see people crying—but they are laughing, thus it is nonsense.

The little old woman across from them does not laugh. Again and again she says the same thing to her neighbors and to the customers: "Because I've done so much harm—that's why they are locking me up! How can it be? I haven't wronged anyone *that* much yet!"

As she talks she rocks her old head to and fro. Sometimes she cries because she does not understand. Perhaps the others, who are laughing, understand more about it— although it seems *very* difficult to understand.

"Lady, don't cry about it," calls the father to the other side. "As long as we are within this fence, no one can hurt us."

But suddenly a quarrel breaks out in the corner of the

48

market. With hoarse voices they shout at each other. It has to do with money that is no longer lying on the counter or that has not been paid. You cannot hear what it is about exactly, but she has the feeling that this is worse than being locked up in a fence.

The policeman at the entrance is standing with his back to the quarrel. He is there only to make sure that no non-Jews go inside the fence. What happens there inside the fence is the Jews' own problem.

That is the Jews' own problem. That is *her* problem. For suddenly she hears that this is not shouting cruel remarks and not a quarrel, but crying, terrible, terrible crying. The skinny little man who is calling for his money and who wants to hit the other man, and the fat fellow who is stopping him, and the man with the white face who has not paid or has taken money away or has perhaps done nothing at all, and all those men and women who are meddling—they are weeping more bitterly than she ever thought grown-ups could do. They are weeping about the fence that closes off the Jewish market and about the policeman who is standing in front of the gate and about the "J" on their identification cards—and they are weeping because she has been sent away from school, though she has done nothing wrong.

Why shouldn't she weep with all those people who are only acting like they are having a quarrel? Genuine, quiet weeping, without pretending to shout?

She does weep, with shaking that seems to tear her apart inside and with tears that she does not attempt to dry at all.

There are no customers, and no one notices it. Only the little old woman on the other side must have seen it, for even though there are no customers to hear her, she wails, "Because that sheep has done so much harm—that's why they are locking her up! How can it be?"

She rocks her old head to and fro and weeps, too, because she does not understand.

After Eight

FATHER AND MOTHER are more handsome than other fathers and mothers, and mother certainly has more dresses than other mothers. Some dresses reach all the way down to the floor, dresses that are very long at the bottom with almost nothing on top. When she has that kind of dress on, it means that father and mother will not be at home in the evening, and that is very unpleasant. But the worst thing is that you cannot even trust the ordinary dresses, the ones that are short on the bottom and closed at the top, for she goes out with that kind of dress on, too. You can always notice it a little bit; if she smells extra nice and if she spends a long time curling her hair, hair that a short time ago suddenly became blond—before that it was only brown, just like father's hair and his—then there is something amiss.

There is always someone at home, but so what? The old woman who has rented a room in their house babysits for him. He does not see her, but he knows that she is there, and that always makes some difference. Still, it is dreary without father and mother; you listen to every sound and can hardly fall asleep.

But now something pleasant has happened. He himself heard it read from the newspaper, and later he heard everyone talking about it with frightened faces and sad voices. No one noticed how happy he was, and he will not say anything about it, since everyone finds it so terrible.

Jews are not allowed on the street after eight o'clock. They must remain in their own homes. There are a lot of other things that they may no longer do, but that does not concern him.

Isn't he lucky that father and mother are Jews? Now they can never again go away when he is in bed. And visitors cannot come, either, for most of their visitors were Jewish—thus he has his parents to himself.

Everyone praises him because he goes to bed so sweetly and quickly in the evenings; they were not used to his doing that. Father and mother and the old woman do not know that it is no longer a great feat to go sweetly to bed, as long as you know that father and mother will remain at home!

Almost no one rings the doorbell after eight. Of course not—who would be calling! But the few times that the doorbell does ring, through the inside door he hears his mother give a frightened scream, and he hears his father say, "That is just someone playing a joke." He himself is never frightened anymore, for father and mother are at home!

Then one night the doorbell rings and it is *not* someone playing a joke. He hears heavy steps going to the living room and some men's voices that receive answers from father and mother. They are of course policemen in black or green uniforms who want to take them away, but father and mother will see to it that nothing happens—you can count on it!

He hears something said about "other rooms." Then the door to his room opens, and his eyes blink against the light. It is father and mother and two policemen in black; he has guessed correctly. Mother's face is very white—not from powder but from fear. She is frightened, of course; he is not.

"Whose child is that?" they ask.

As if he would be lying in bed here in this house if he weren't father's and mother's child!

Father says that he is theirs.

"He is seven years old," he adds. As if that has anything to do with it! He is a little annoyed because everyone always thinks that he is older, and now that he is lying in bed, the policemen in black cannot see how big he is.

"You can stay," says one. "The papers are in order. Are there more people in the house?" He sees how father reflects a little. Perhaps he will fib about the old woman.

He blushes when he thinks about it, and father does, too. The one policeman in black has surely seen that, for suddenly he shouts in a very loud voice, "If you lie, then all of you will go!"

He puts his head under the covers in terror. Let father say it—let father tell the truth about the old woman!

A bit hoarsely father says, "We have a room that we rent to an elderly lady." Now he dares to come out from under the covers, and he just sees that father is going out of the room with the two men. Mother leans against the wall and cries. "Oh, God!" she says. It is a shame that she is crying, but it is cozy for him that she is staying with him.

He does not hear any crying coming from the room of the old woman, thus perhaps she may remain here, too. He snuggles deeper into the covers; he will let mother cry, for he cannot change that. It takes a long time with the old woman; while he waits he sleeps a little. But then he hears someone saying loudly, "Come on, now, but hurry," and then the old woman comes in to him. She has her coat on and her hat on and a heavy load bound to her back. Father carries yet another suitcase for her. She is crying very softly—there are only tears and a face that seems to be laughing and hurting at the same time.

"Goodbye, child—goodbye, boy," she says in a very high voice. "Give me a kiss, darling—I must go." He no longer kisses women, really, because he is too big for that, but now that the old woman must go away with the policemen in black uniforms, that is something else again. He comes out from under the covers, but he does not need to sit erect in bed, for the old woman is so small and her face is so bent over and close because of the heavy load on her back. Very carefully he gives her a little kiss on her wet face and says, "Goodbye, have a good trip."

"Hurry," says the man at the door. Father supports the heavy pack from underneath. Both he and mother go with them to the front door; fortunately they may go no further, for it is after eight.

When they come back to him in his room, mother

weeps again, leaning against father. Quietly he waits until most of the crying is over and then asks if he may go into the living room. He knows very well that he will be allowed to do anything, now that the policemen in black uniforms have come and have taken the old woman away.

And in the living room, with father and mother together with him and with the light on, he thinks about how fortunate it is that they are not allowed to go out the door after eight. Otherwise the old woman would have been taken away, and he would have been alone in the house—or they would have taken him away, too, because father would not have been there to show them the papers.

Instead of lying in bed now, he is sitting with both of them in the living room. He rubs himself against the back of the chair, thoroughly happy.

Isn't he lucky?

Disaster

IT HAPPENED IN one moment, in one terrible moment: the school, full of star girls, shook and thundered—the corridor was full of flames and smoke—then the school seemed to be made of glass, which was breaking—and then the flames disappeared and there was only smoke and dust—and splinters, a corridor full of splinters. And above one place in the corridor you saw the blue sky through the two stories of the building.

Then out of all the classroom doors came women with pale faces and girls with pale faces, and then all those feet found a way through the splinters of glass, down the steps. Suddenly they were standing outside in the glaring sunlight.

They do not know what happened. They are silent from terror and dismay. A few girls begin to cry softly, but most of them only look into each other's white faces in alarm.

Mothers from the neighborhood come running. They *can* make a sound, because they have come from outside. They *can* shout out their emotions when they find their children unhurt. For not one of them has a scratch. Not one of the hundreds of star girls was in the corridor when the shell exploded on that part of the roof that no longer exists now. Five minutes before the explosion they *had* been in the corridor, for everyone had been walking in groups to another room. They do not yet understand how it is that they are standing outside there unharmed and all together—the mothers and passersby, girls and teachers. A few begin to laugh in high and shrill voices at the black dust on their faces and at their lopsided cooking caps; a few who at first looked around in bewilderment begin to cry.

A fire engine drives up. The men go inside. At the same time men from the civil defense come, too. The children look searchingly into the faces that they see go past them and into the school. Are they friends of the Jews or do they wish to harm them? Don't you ask that about each person who does not wear a star? Formerly you did not; there was no difference then, and when someone went inside your school or your house, you merely nodded to him without thinking. How long ago that is!

They begin to talk softly. Ordinary voices, without laughter or crying, bring a feeling of deliverance to them. An adult speaks out, "How quietly and calmly you went outside—you little heroines!"

Then a large, bony girl says in a flat voice, "Is it so awful? If we had been in the corridor, we would be dead. Is that so terrible? One night last week I sat for three hours in a closet, until they were gone. My little brother sat in the gutter—and it was raining. I called to him that he could come in, for they had gone. Father and mother were gone, too. The house was empty. You don't dare turn a light on, because they might still notice that someone is in the house. It's a pretty good trick not to scream as the school comes thundering down!"

She walks away as if she were angry at the person who called them heroines. But over her shoulder she adds, "And at least you are all in this together!"

Promenade

THERE WAS A time—how long ago was it? Months ago! There was a time when you were allowed to be old and sick. It was then a stroke of luck when someone in your house was sick; everyone was allowed to stay at home then, at least if that person was very ill, and preferably contagious. There were children who got scarlet fever just in time—not intentionally, but they really did get it—and that would be sufficient for them to remain at home for many weeks. But in the end an illness passes, and the sick child may die, too, and then the illness does no good anymore.

But suddenly that is changed; now they come take the sick and the elderly away. They do not have to wait until after eight, for those who are very old and very sick, those who cannot walk and those who have not been out on the street in years—those people are at home during the day as well. A long truck comes in front of the door, a truck in which sick people from other houses are lying. The men who have come to fetch them are Jews who wear suits with a star on the breast and an SS on the sleeve. They carry the sick on stretchers from their beds to the truck. It goes very quickly. It is difficult only when those sick people live very high, up narrow, straight stairs. Yet they all end up in the truck eventually, and when it is full, it is first emptied in the building from where the sick are sent away, and then the truck can continue to take away more sick people.

He knows precisely how it is done, for a lot of elderly people live near him in the neighborhood, and when he was not in too much of a hurry to go to school, he stood and watched. The first time he was terribly frightened by it; he accidentally saw the face of an old woman on the stretcher, and he never wants to see that again, for it is so difficult to forget. And the people who were also standing there watching softly uttered terrible curses at the Jews who were taking the old people away. They did not curse loudly because of the men in green uniforms who were there watching. But the Jews who take the old people away cannot help it, for they have to do it.

During subsequent times, he would always want to keep walking in order not to see such a face again, but again and again he could not stop himself; he *had* to look. Thus he knows precisely how it is done.

But there is something else in his neighborhood that is perhaps just as terrible. There are many elderly people, or people with a crippled leg, or people with crutches, or people who shake badly—people who naturally have not walked outside or who have been bedridden all those years. But if they remain in their homes now, they are hauled away. Therefore they do their best to come out and be on the street. The whole day—for those men could come at any time during the day to take them.

He meets them in the morning as he is going to school. He knows some of them. Some he does not see again after a few days; they were taken away, then, because they could not remain on the street day and night, or they have died because they were much too sick to keep walking on the street. He misses them for a little while, one or two days, but then everything continues as usual.

They all speak to him when he meets them. Not just a little chat to be social: they all have something to ask him and every star child or star person whom they meet. Again and again they ask each one the same thing. They point with their head or their cane or their trembling finger to the street from where you have just come and ask, "Is it quiet there?"

He knows what "quiet" means. It has nothing to do with quiet or with a quiet street. It can be as busy as you like. It means: that there are no men in green or black—that they are not busy taking people from their homes in that street—that there are no trucks waiting to take sick people away. When it actually is quiet, he says "yes" and nods to them because he really does like them all. But a few times he had to say no, and his throat was closed so tightly that all he could do was shake his head. Then those elderly people turned around and went back to the street from where they had just come. One old woman who was standing with her back toward him began to cry very loudly. He cried too, softly and very unhappily. Fortunately he had stopped by the time he got to school.

There is one little old man whom he calls his friend. He has thick bandages on both his feet, and because he cannot get shoes on over them, he has large, worn-down slippers fastened under his feet. He cannot walk in them, of course, but only shuffle along. When it is dry weather it goes well, but when it rains and there are puddles everywhere, then the slippers and the cloth bandages are completely wet. Yet there is nothing to be done about it, for Jews may not ride in a tram—and how expensive it would be to keep riding back and forth in the tram! And staying at home because of the miserable weather is much too dangerous.

He does not know himself why this little man is his friend. It is because of the white beard, perhaps, or the manner in which he asks, "Is it quiet there?" He never had a grandpa, but he would like to have such a grandpa as his friend—only without those bandages on the feet and with ordinary shoes on.

Then a day comes, a soaking-wet day—he himself has top boots and a cape on—and on this day he meets many fewer old people. He does not meet his friend, either.

Surely they have ventured to stay at home; if they are

taken away, it is still drier in the truck than being out on the street the whole day. It is actually sensible of them to stay at home.

Most of them are there again the next day. His friend is not. And on all the days that follow—all the days during which they ask him as usual if it is quiet there—during all those days he does not see his friend anymore. He himself notices how he is on the lookout for him. After a week he does not look for him anymore; he knows that his friend with the bandaged feet will not be coming back.

The worst thing is that he does not know whether his friend has been taken away or whether he has died. Both are terrible things. He does not want to be dead or taken away for a long time. But when someone is your friend, you still have to know what has happened to him.

Weeks, weeks later, when there are no longer any elderly, sick people walking about because they have all been taken away now, he begins to believe that his friend is dead. It is more pleasant to believe that. For if he is dead, he no longer has to be afraid of the rain, which makes his slippers and the cloths around his feet wet. And if he is dead, he no longer has to ask at every corner, "Is it quiet there?"

Yes, it is much more pleasant if his friend is dead. But he himself does not want to be dead for a long time, oh, not for a *long* time!

Shopping

YOU ARE ALLOWED to go to the stores only between three and five o'clock. Of course, you may go the whole day to the stores that are marked as Jewish stores, but there are some things that you cannot get there, and then you must go to another shop. It is a pity that you are usually not free between three and five; therefore you must wait until you finally have an afternoon off.

Today she and mother are both free, and between three and five they will go to the shopping district. She has looked forward to it as if it were a holiday, for it has been such a long time since she has been out of the Jewish quarter. She may no longer go back and forth to school, and it is forbidden to go outside the city; ice skating, now that the ice is so fine, is forbidden. Going to the park is forbidden. How, then, do you get to leave the Jewish quarter?

With her arm linked in mother's she skips along, just as she skipped when she was six years old and went to school for the first time or when mother brought her to a party. She is now too old for it, really, for she is just as big as mother, and anyone can see that she will grow much larger. But ever since the difficult and dreary times came about outside the house, inside the house she has become more childish than ever. She demands mother's undivided attention as soon as she can get hold of her and begs for the little habits of earlier times as if they had never been given up.

They walk along the busy shopping street. They have already done much of their shopping; it has not been as cheerful or as pleasant as she had imagined it would be. But from this shopping street, which used to be the high point of excitement and light and marvelous things behind glass, she expects compensation for what in the other streets is unavailable.

There are not many people with stars walking about. They are allowed to be here, however, for otherwise there would be a board at the beginning of the street with "Jews forbidden" written upon it, and the police would have sent them away immediately. She looks at the people they meet to see if they are wearing a star or to see if they are perhaps looking unkindly at their stars. You just do not know anymore; when the stars were new, many people took their hats off to your star out of respect and because they had found the situation so terrible. Now everyone is used to it; you no longer know if they want to make you disappear or if they would have taken their hats off to you, as if a Jew with a star had not become such an ordinary figure.

"We used to drink a cup of chocolate there," she says, reveling in the memory. The fact that there is now a sign on the door of the milk bar marked "Jews forbidden" does not bother her too much. She gladly loses herself in the past. Events of the present she takes in stride. Events of bygone days are the only pleasant things for her to think about.

They are now standing in front of the window of a music store. Their own piano has been out of the house since the time the deportations began. It would be such a pity to leave the piano behind. But you can look through music books and check on what you have and have not played, even if you no longer have a piano. And you can imagine that you are going to the music teacher again with books in your bag, that you will play for him again, as beautifully as you can, more beautifully than you played in the best moments at home in that week.

"A recorder..." she suddenly dreams, mollified. "You can play that, too, and you can carry it in your rucksack if you're taken away..."

Did she say that aloud? Mother looks at her with a sideward glance, and then with a sudden motion pulls her to the door. She does not immediately know how she stands, but then she hears mother say, "You shall have a recorder. You can't make music on paper money, but you can on a recorder."

In the empty store they must wait for a salesperson to come. She looks eagerly around at all the music books and instruments. She already knows which recorder she will choose—that dark brown one, which is actually waiting for her to buy it.

A saleswoman with brazen-blond hair comes down the steps to the store. She looks first at their faces, then lower, at their stars.

"Ladies, you are not wanted here," she says in a high voice and points to a sign that is hanging in the store and that they have not seen: "Jews not wanted."

In the street, a bit dizzy, she clamps her arm tightly around mother's. "Let's just go home," she says wearily.

Safety

THE WORST THING of all is that mother and father are so afraid for her. It is worse than the roundups and police vans and everything else that is threatening them—that father and mother want to keep her and themselves and all their valuables safe.

There are many prohibitions for Jews listed each week in the Jewish newspaper. Now and then the big newspapers list them, too, when the others must know what is forbidden to Jews and when they must know what contact with Jews is forbidden to them. But most of the prohibitions are not known to the other people, because they are listed only in the Jewish paper. It is easier to remember the things permitted than the things prohibited, because there is hardly anything permitted.

But of the few things that are allowed, there is still a lot that is forbidden by father and mother, because they are so afraid and because they want to hide her and everything they have from danger. That is the worst of all. Every day other girls do as much as the paper states is allowed; they derive as much pleasure from each day as is still possible. If those girls are taken from their homes tomorrow, then at least they have had today and yesterday.

But father and mother take every day away from her

because they want to see to it that she will not be deported tomorrow. As if you are not going to be hauled away in the end! A little bit sooner or a little bit later, what difference does it make? If father and mother and she must go away later than the others, won't they still have had a more miserable time than anyone else because of their watching out for their safety? What good is that?

Because she is already sixteen years old she has an identification card. Some Jews can get their cards stamped with a Z, which for a time can prevent them from being deported. You can be a student at a special school, where all the students get a Z; you can hold a job that is considered indispensable. Oh, there are more ways to be able to stay for a while, you just have to know what to do. All the thousands who have been deported did not know how, or they did something—or did not do something—for which they received instead of a Z, an S, a punishment S, on their identification cards. But of course father knows precisely how you can attain a Z. He once sent her to a school where she felt very ill at ease because all the boys and girls were allowed to do much more than she. But there was a rest home for old men and women in the neighborhood of that school, and when the Nazis wanted to rid the country of the elderly and consequently emptied the rest homes, father and mother found it too dangerous for her, and she was no longer allowed to attend the school. Then father found a job for her. The job was actually not indispensable at all, but it kept the Z on her identification card. Besides, he has seen to it that the Z on his own identification card applies to her, too, and that makes her doubly safe.

Her job, which is so indispensable, leaves her with some free time, but what good does it do her? If a friend comes to pick her up to visit another girl who lives in another, distant Jewish quarter, then father and mother find it too dangerous for her to go so far from home; a roundup can occur on the way, and you are still safest at home. Sometimes she revolts and reproaches them that they are taking everything that she might still have away from her. Then they speak calmly and reasonably to her, and speaking calmly and reasonably is even worse. Father and mother say that it is for her own good. Up till now her whole life has been destroyed for her own good—but she is unable to explain that to them!

Then a night comes when they were taken from their house with an S—in spite of all the double Z's. They do not know why, and the man who takes them away does not know, either, he says. They have no rucksacks ready because they were *so* safe that a rucksack did not seem necessary. They have fifteen minutes to pack. Fifteen minutes is not much time, especially if you have been roused from your sleep, to dress yourself for a winter in Poland and to take along some food. As they stand in the street in the darkened night, they know that they have forgotten the most essential things, but they are not permitted to go back.

And she feels a joy, a joy that radiates over all the terror and misery and that she will never discuss with anyone. There is joy in that it has come, that she can no longer be looked after and fussed over from all sides now; there is joy because a way out is no longer possible, and above all because she is going away, far away from the daily routine of going from her house to work, from work to her house. It does not matter where she is going. She no longer has to wait for what is coming, for it has come.

This joy makes her feel ashamed and sinful. Among the many silent, heavily laden Jews with whom she has been shoved into a night tram, she feels liberated and alone. If only she could tell the others how good it is not to have to wait for the danger anymore! No one would be able to understand it.

They wait to be transported further in the dirty, stuffy theater that serves as their prison. The next day those whose cases are irrevocable are put in a tram that brings them to the train station. But her case and father's and mother's cases are not irrevocable. Their cases are worked upon and studied; influence is used. The days and nights among the seething mass of people who know neither rest nor sleep continue for nearly a week.

Her feelings of joy and liberation have long since left her. Again there is a way out being sought, again the protection from all sides. Will she never be like the others, who are taken and deported and who know that this happens to them and to every other Jew? But this—she does not want this any longer...

On the fourth day she screams out that she does not want this any longer. She want to go away, she wants to be deported, she no longer wants all that bungling and lingering...

The people around her look at her with eyes dulled by the long days and nights. Mother wraps her arms around her.

"Be quiet—quiet—let father take care of it. Father will get us out."

"But I don't *want* to get out! I don't want to go home! I want to go to Poland!"

They think that she is suffering from nervous strain, and they bring her all the way up the steps to the sick ward. As they are laying her on a mattress that has just been left vacant by someone else, she lets them go. Next to her is a man in the midst of an asthma attack, and with swollen eyes she watches him fearfully as he fights for air. Behind her she hears vomiting, horrible, choking vomiting. There is groaning and wailing everywhere. Oh, she is so overwrought, but she will surely come to her senses here...

In spite of it all she falls asleep. She has not lain down since she was taken out of her bed four nights ago; they have been able only to sit on the plush folding seats of the theater. Now she sleeps a dreamless sleep and awakens in artificial light. She does not immediately recognize the sounds of despair all around her, but when she recognizes them she springs hot-tempered from her mattress and says to the nurse that she is rested. She can go back to her mother now.

Mother is sleeping; her head is hanging over on her breast, and her hands, which have let go of her bag holding all their most important belongings, are resting in her lap. Before she goes to sit next to mother she quietly picks up the bag, grasps it firmly, and holds it on her knees. They cannot get along without that bag if they go to Poland. She wants to go to Poland.

But on the sixth day father's ceaseless drive and questions and efforts have succeeded. They may return home.

Their house has been plundered. Whatever they had that was worth anything is gone. There is nothing to eat. But the beds are still standing just as they were when she and father and mother had crawled out of them.

This will be her prison, more anxiously guarded than before. She will not be allowed to do anything, she will not be allowed to go anywhere. She has returned to safety.

Perhaps...perhaps...if after one week, after two weeks, they are *again* taken away, and if it does not succeed a second time...

Dawn

SINCE MOTHER'S DEATH he has depended entirely on father. He sleeps in father's room and is not afraid of the men in green or the men in black, who could come any night to take them.

But now a man who has been father's friend ever since their childhood is in the hospital, dying. He has tried to take his own life; he was so alone that he did not feel it worthwhile to wait to see whether he was going to be deported.

Boys who are twelve years old must not know about such things.

But boys who are twelve years old have ears, boys who are ten and eight and six years old, too—and you cannot help that you hear and understand these things!

He understands, too, that father does not want to leave his friend alone in the night to die. Father must be with his friend. But father must also be with his son, otherwise the men in green or black might come to take him just on that night and he cannot explain to them that he belongs with father. Jews may never leave their homes after eight. But if you are sitting up with one who is dying, then you are allowed to break that curfew. Father may stay at the hospital. Perhaps the men in green will come tonight to raid the hospital, but that does not matter, because father is allowed to be there.

But what is he to do? He has no friend who wants to die and for whom he may keep watch; boys his age do not yet want to die because they are always thinking that there is still a chance for some good in the world. No, he may not go with father and stay at the hospital.

But then a solution is found: if the men in green raid the hospital, they must find the boy in the same ward as father, just as if he, too, is sitting up with father's friend.

There is no extra bed in that ward. But a long, cozy lounge chair is made up as a real bed and set in the bathroom for him. He crawls in, supremely content and relaxed, and falls asleep at once.

Jews are not allowed on the street before six o'clock in the morning. Otherwise father would have awakened him and taken him home, for father's friend died when it was still dark. Now father comes at six to wake him so that he can get dressed and go home.

The boy stretches in the warm bed and smiles at father.

"I had such a good sleep," he says.

Father smiles back, but his face is very pale because he did not go to bed and because his friend has taken his own life.

Morning is just beginning to break as the two comrades come through the large gate of the hospital in the street along the canal. The air coming through the bare trees is pale with light stripes. He shivers a little because he has just gotten out of bed; he shoves his hands deep into his pockets and walks silently next to father. He would like to ask questions about father's friend and about dying, but he feels that father would rather not talk about it now.

Then father suddenly grasps him by the shoulder. He is startled by it, and both of them stand still. Father points his finger to the other side of the canal. There they see a small group of Jews; there are men, women, and children, heavily laden and wearily dragging their feet. They are moving very slowly, for their rucksacks would be heavy even for a strong man to carry, and there are no strong men among these people.

"These are the lucky ones," says father. "They were taken from their homes last night, and they may now return to them. They had to wait until six o'clock, but now they are going home."

Father's hand still lies heavily on his shoulder, even as he walks further and says, "Remember what you have seen there."

When father has removed his hand from his shoulder, the question that he has been holding back comes involuntarily to his lips.

"Father, what is it like to die?"

Father smiles gently as he answers.

"It's not bad, son. It's not bad at all."

Transfer

THE YOUNG MOTHER has waited until it is dark outside; that was the agreement, for you may not do such a thing as this in the daylight.

She has dressed the dancing little girl in many clothes. Her daughter has never been out in the dark, and furthermore she does not have to put so much in the suitcase if the child has on a lot of clothes.

"We're going to a puppet show, aren't we?" the little girl cheers in a high voice, again and again.

How has the child come upon the words puppet show? The mother has not said so to the little girl; she has not wanted to tell a lie. Perhaps because going out in the evening is festive and because a puppet show sounds festive...

"Ready," she says. "Now say goodbye to father and give him a kiss, because we're going out."

As the child stands on her toes by father and puckers her lips for a kiss, the man looks up helplessly at his young wife, who nods at him with a tight smile. Her smile says, "No farewells. Haven't we decided that she must leave us joyously?"

"Goodbye, little one," he says. "Have a good time."

"We're going to a puppet show!" is the last thing that he hears from her.

On the way, in the darkened streets, the little voice prattles without stop.

"Why is it so dark in the street?"

"Because the moon is still sleeping."

"But it's light at the puppet show, isn't it?"

"Oh, yes."

Amid the answers the mother's thoughts are brooding.

"She is blond and she is a girl. Otherwise it would not have been possible. I must be glad that she is blond and a girl. I must be glad that she is leaving me."

"And I don't have to go to bed for a long time, do I?"

"Oh, not for a long, long, long time!"

"Because I've been so good, haven't I?"

"Because you've been so good."

And in her thoughts she asks, "Will you remain good, even when you're with the strangers whom I am not allowed to know because that would be dangerous? Will you still be good when I get you back? Or will I never get you back?"

"Is the puppet show far?"

"I don't know. I'm bringing you to another aunt, and she will take you further."

"Is that other aunt far?"

"No, we'll be there soon."

"Why aren't you going with me to the puppet show?"

"I don't have time."

"Will you come another time?"

"Yes, another time."

"Liars, liars that we are," she thinks, and the suitcase weighs heavily in her hand. With her other hand she is grasping her daughter's little hand tightly.

They arrive at the house of the transfer. A girl will be waiting for her there, a girl who has already transferred many star children and who has kept the secret of the new house to herself. She is the one who asked for a blond child, a girl.

While she goes up the steps with the child, the mother wants to think about the puppet show. The child has thrown the festive thought to her, light as a bouncing ball; now she must catch it. Above on the steps she can actually laugh.

The young girl waiting for her is serious and dedicated to her dangerous work. She must get used to the laughing mother who has a child to give away, perhaps for life. Then the girl continues the game, the game of the puppet show illusion; she will take it upon herself to make the illusion come true as soon as the child has arrived at her new home.

"Are you going with me now?" asks the child, impatient to enjoy the end of the happy adventure.

"Yes," says the girl. "You must say goodbye to mother now."

She is used to pulling and tearing children away while her own heart is threatening to break in the process. It will be different here: this mother dares to laugh.

The child gives her mother a hurried kiss.

"Goodbye! I don't have to go to bed for a long time?"

"No," says the mother, and the puppet show illusion

is now inadequate. "Goodbye—goodbye, little one—have a good time."

The child now watches attentively.

"Are you sad because you can't come with me?"

The mother only nods and looks up helplessly at the young girl as if to tell her that she must take her daughter away now and end this torment.

The child speaks up with a second kiss and with emphasis on each word.

"If you *don't* cry then *you* may come with me next time. All right?"

White Lie

IT IS DIFFICULT enough for everyone in the city to get food, but it is even more difficult for the Jews. The Jewish fish stores are not permitted to sell fish, and the Jewish greengroceries may not sell fruit but only those vegetables that are left over in the city. The fish stores have merely a few jars of mustard and a little beet salad displayed in the windows. The greengroceries have a lot of turnips at the moment because the people in the city cannot eat all the turnips up. A while ago there were absolutely no vegetables left over. At that time he and father found a little spot one afternoon, a spot where a "Jews forbidden" sign did not stand but that was green nevertheless, and there they picked nettles together. They tasted all right when mother had cooked them—you would almost say that the nettles had been bought in a store.

Of course, you are not permitted to go into a non-Jewish fish store or grocery store, not even between three and five, thus it is difficult enough. And just once they would so like to eat some fruit. Some people get fruit in a package sent from outside the city, but oh, that is dangerous, for if the men in green come after eight o'clock to take you away and if they find apple peelings in your garbage can, even though you say that you have gotten apples from outside the city, nevertheless you and everyone else in the house will be punished. One time they themselves received a fish from a friend of father's who is not Jewish and who thus is allowed to fish. When the fish was eaten, they threw the bones into the toilet because it would have been dangerous to have thrown them into the garbage can. And someone rang their doorbell that evening! Luckily it was not the police but a person who wanted to go to some neighbors of theirs but who came to their house by mistake. They were frightened nevertheless, and happy, too, that there were no fishbones lying in the garbage can!

Now mother wants so very much to have apples for father's birthday, and there is a way to get them, but it is a bit dangerous. He wants to get them just because it *is* dangerous. He is eight years old but is so small that he could pass for six. And six years old is not much different from five, and if you are five, you do not have to wear a star. Of course he always wears a star, but he has a sweater without a star. Understand? And he is blond, too. He can walk into a non-Jewish grocery and buy two kilograms of apples! Easy enough!

Mother does not find it as easy as he does. He might meet people there who know that he is a little Jewish boy. There might be people there who ask him what his last name is, and their last name sounds Jewish.

"If they ask you why you aren't wearing a star, say that you're five."

"All right," he nods, reassured. He is suddenly happy with his small size, which he has always found so terribly humiliating.

"And if they ask you your name, say that...say that it's DeJong. That can be both."

71

"DeJong," he repeats softly. There are Jewish children at school whose names are DeJong, but mother says that it can be both, so that is all right. DeJong.

All is going well. No one asks him why he is not wearing a star. Being without a star is really a pleasant feeling. When he sees a man in green, he thinks, "He can't do anything to me because he doesn't know that I'm Jewish." It really is a pleasant feeling.

He must wait a long time in the store. There are many women who come before him. When it is his turn, he comes to the counter, his head just reaching above it.

"Two kilograms of apples," he says immediately. He has such a craving for apples.

While she is weighing the fruit, the woman begins to talk to him. She is friendly because he is so small.

"What is your name, little one?"

He must reflect a bit.

"DeJong," he says.

"No," smiles the woman. "I mean your first name."

He has not counted on this. His first name? He does not know whether Jopie is a Jewish name or whether it can be both. Still it would be better not to say Jopie. But what, then?

"Come on, tell me," nods the woman.

"Jesus," he says hoarsely.

Baby in the Basket

THERE HAVE BEEN other times in which little star babies were punished because they were so foolish to have been born. There have been other times in which star mothers hid their babies somewhere in order to keep them alive. There have been other times in which star mothers had to flee with their new babies. Oh, what is happening now is so old, so old.

The newborn babies cannot help that they have been so foolish. No one warned them. They naturally dreamed of a completely different world when they were still enveloped by their mothers' warmth. They dreamed of safety and rest, of light and love. You are allowed to be so foolish when you are not yet born. It is not fair that you are punished for your foolishness as soon as you are born.

This star baby is very small indeed, and it surely could have stayed inside its mother for a bit longer. But there was much anxiety in mother because father was picked up during a roundup and immediately deported. Thus the baby preferred to be born. Now it is lying in a cradle that is still much too large; it will not be growing into it, either, for when it is six weeks old it may be taken away with mother. They think that six weeks is long enough to lie in a cradle and grow in this world, this world that is so different from what the baby has dreamed about.

The mother is still lying in bed, and day and night she thinks about the other mothers of long ago who hid their babies or fled with them. She would like to ask them, "How did you do it? How did you find the way that you had to go? And the milk, then, that you had to give your baby? And were you also so afraid? Did you also have a lump in your throat each time your child drank your milk and you did not know how long you would be able to do it?"

Those other mothers cannot answer because they are all long dead, and thus the new mother is not finding a way out.

But one day a mother who is young and living comes to her, and she has answers to the questions. She is allowed to keep her baby because she is not a star mother. Years ago when they were still girls, they thought that stars existed only high in the heavens and could not be taken down below to be used to chase people forth and surrender them unprotected. Years ago when they were still girls, they sat next to each other in school. They have never forgotten that.

Well—everything sounds so simple, then. For this mother can certainly take care of two small children instead of one, can't she?

"But he's so small!"

"He'll grow."

"And the milk, then!"

"I have enough milk for two."

The mothers of long ago smile. And the little baby in the oversized cradle believes that it was not *so* very foolish to have been born, after all.

2. *Star House*

A Laundry Basket Full

THEY COME ON the one night and leave on the next. Two days ago they received a summons; there is nothing more to be done now. Oh yes, there are a few who do not pay attention to the threats and remain at home, people who believe that they cannot keep track exactly of who has and who has not come. And there are others who in the two days still saw a chance to hide. But most know that there is nothing more to be done; they come on the one night and leave on the next. It must still happen at night, in the dark, because the city is not yet used to the dragging away of Jews, and the people might rebel if they should see it. The trams pick up the Jews in the darkened street in front of the Star House, a building that used to be called a theater. The trams carry the Jews off, leaving no traces behind, and when the city comes to life at four o'clock the next morning, the dusky street will not betray what has happened there in the darkness. It really is well-planned; the city will remain calm, and the transport can go further, undisturbed. Later, months later, when the city has gradually become used to everything, a summons and the darkness of night will no longer be necessary; then Jews will be taken out of their homes without preparation, at any hour of the night or day.

Then the old and the sick, the crippled and the dying will go as well, those who were lulled by safety. Then it will no longer be called "employment of Jews in Germany" because the dying cannot be put to work. Then it will no longer need a name that appears just, for by then the city will be used to it all.

They are called up between the ages of sixteen and forty-five, although parents under forty-five must take their children under sixteen. And so they stream into the Star House, from children a few months old to men and women of forty-five. Darkness protects them from the glances of the city but not from the air fight high above their heads, of which the city is warned by wailing sirens. The sirens have not shrieked for them because they must be at the theater on time; without the participants the show cannot begin.

And if the splinters of shells should rain down upon them and their children, what difference would it make? This is the end, all the same. A shell splinter would be more merciful. The deafening evil in the air is the sound installation of the horror show that will be presented in the theater. But no one in the audience shudders at this horror show; shuddering you do only when your fantasy is stirred by harsh means. This is real.

Real are the crying voices of children in the wings, the lobbies, in the balconies, the amphitheaters, on the steps, in the pit, in the hall. Real are the voices of babies who were used to sleeping between the evening and morning feedings and who have now left their secluded rooms for good. Real are the voices of young children who are laid down upon straw mattresses in the wings— for mothers with little children receive a mattress instead of a folding seat in the theater area—and the children must try to sleep because it is night. They cannot sleep, for along the open side of their sleeping area people are continually streaming in. The children do not want to sleep because these are not their own beds, their own bedrooms, and because so many terrible things can happen to them, and while they sleep their mothers can

78

leave them. They cannot, they do not want to sleep—and yet they are so terribly tired.

Real is the shuffling of feet up the steps, down the steps—real and endless. Real is the groaning and lamenting under the nook of the roof where the sick ward has been set up—real and unbearable—unbearable.

But real is also the laughter of the very young people; they are seeking adventure or a difficult task in the sudden collapse of the protecting or restricting walls of a fostering or all-too-binding home. They are seeking each other, the boys the boys and the girls the girls; sometimes the boys and girls are seeking each other, and without knowing it they give each other the support that was taken from them when the doors of their safe homes were slammed shut behind them. Oh, they are real as they laugh and talk and as they are quiet, with lips pressed tightly together.

Whenever a new group arrives, each within the allotted time of one hour, the curtain goes aside, the curtain that hides the light of the hall from the darkened street. Then there are hands that pull them inside, that take the children or the baggage, that point the way further inside. But the children do not let themselves be taken from their mothers; they weigh heavily in the weary arms, and they blink in the sudden light and look shyly at the men in uniforms who are keeping watch there. They want nothing of this strangeness and harshness and terror. The mothers can do nothing other than hold them in their arms the whole time, including the mothers who are squatting on the mattresses, whose children do not allow themselves to be laid down.

Some people run through the curtain into the hall, fleeing from the hell of the shelling outside to the hell there inside; they are fleeing from the grip of the one devil into the arms of another. Oh, it is a hit, this show in the theater!

But the two young women carrying a big laundry basket between them do not run inside. Because of the basket the curtain must be put a bit further aside for them. They do not run inside, they cannot. They shuffle slowly just as they did the whole way to the theater, even when the air raid alarm began to shriek, even when the splinters of shells fell around them. They cannot go faster because the load between them is too big and too breakable.

"Two," calls the assistant by the curtain inside. For the harvest of people must be counted.

"Four," calls the one young woman softly. The way was long and the laundry basket was difficult to carry, otherwise she would have said it loudly.

The assistant does not want to be confused; again the curtain goes aside and again he must call a number. He beckons the women with the laundry basket to go further inside; there the baggage will be taken over.

But the baggage cannot be taken over. The two women set the basket down in the middle of the shuffling feet. They turn back the cloth that is lying over it.

One cannot discern very well what is moving there—but something is moving. There in the basket is a foundation of cloths and tiny clothes—on top lie the blankets—and under the blanket and at the one end of it something is moving. Oh, it is only something small—not worth troubling about. The little sound that is coming from the basket is also not worth troubling about, certainly not against the noise and shouting inside and the thunder of the defense outside.

"I didn't know it," said the assistant, feeling foolish. "I couldn't know that!"

"No," says the woman who is the mother.

"But they are newborn," says the man who is bending over the laundry basket. "They don't have to go then!"

"They were premature," says the mother. "That doesn't count. They are four months old."

"But..." says the man, dismayed, stupefied, "but why..."

Then the mother calls, and it sounds out above all the noise, "Because their father has never seen them—*that's* why—and because they have done so much harm—*that's* why!"

Harmonica

HE DOES NOT know that this Star House is hell. How should he know? For he has his harmonica with him, and as long as he has that, then heaven is everywhere.

He is together with father—two comrades who are voluntarily going after mother. A few days ago she was picked up in a roundup and sent away. What must they do here now, without her? Perhaps they can catch up with her and then be sent further away together. They packed their rucksacks together, father and he, with the most necessary items, and then they walked bravely to the Star House. He put his harmonica in his rucksack, for how can he go after mother and be sent further on, to Poland or who-knows-where, without his harmonica?

Father *does* know that this is hell. All the grown-ups know. But father can forget about it for long moments because he has his little boy with him, his little boy with the harmonica. He can forget that the auditorium, the balconies, the festive red seats and the plain wooden folding chairs, the stairs, the corridors, the coffee rooms, he can forget that everything is full of people and full of rumor and complaint. There is the complaint of the children and complaint of the people who are ill or becoming ill and who must cry out their misery. There is the rumor of the rolling, shuffling masses up and down the steps, the calling of those who belong together and cannot reach each other. There is the voice of the announcer above everything, booming through the loudspeaker. *No* place is quiet because there is movement and noise everywhere; there is *no* place to wail or to just die quietly. And yet for long moments father can forget that this is hell because of his little boy with the harmonica.

A woman who does not yet have to be sent away goes among the people and the children and tries to help. How can you help when you are damned and in hell? You must first be redeemed, then. How can you be redeemed now, when the misery of thousands lies on your shoulders and you yourself may not go with them to the unknown ruin? That can only be done by someone who carries a little piece of heaven with him, can't it?

Then she sees the little star boy with the harmonica. In his shining eyes she sees that he has the power to redeem the damned. She wants to, she wants to be redeemed, otherwise she cannot help these thousands. She begs him for a song. He looks anxiously around him and asks for a quiet corner. Of course there isn't one! But in the drafty fire exit where people are dragging rucksacks and heavy baggage, where people are shouting and running, it is somewhat dark; you see no faces there, and the weeping of children is silent. Then he plays for the woman. His eyes look up from above his harmonica, right into hers. He holds her with his eyes. He holds her back from sinking and damnation. His school songs, softly and carefully played, dominate the fire exit with its darkness and din. The echo of an echo song he knows to play even softer than his already small, shy sound. He conquers all that is bad and rough and violent in the world with the pureness of his tune. He dreams of a gently gliding boat. He is pushed against the brick wall by a rucksack being dragged by, but his little boat glides further.

"But now a march," says father. "Are you silly? We must have a march." And the little star boy plays a march.

The woman gives him a kiss because he has redeemed her. Therefore the whole evening, the whole night, she receives winks back from him whenever she passes him on her journeys in this hell. Then they are driven out into the dark night—men and women, children, too, bent forward under the load of all their possessions, infants in fathers' or mothers' arms or in little baskets. They are driven out to the dusky trams that stand waiting in the street and into which they will be shoved. Then the woman walks like a beggar along the trams to see if she can find something of the little star boy and his rucksack and his harmonica. She catches a glimpse of him as the tram begins to leave; she waves and throws him a kiss. He waves back, beaming.

She remains behind in the dark street. She must go back again into the now almost empty building. There are still some assistants there, worn out suddenly now that everything is over again, and there are still some men in uniforms, superfluous now that there is no need to exercise any power. There are some groaning sick people in the sick room, and there is much, much trash and dirt and dust, the silent remains of what has been suffered and has now disappeared.

But she has the tune with her, and she carries it with her throughout that night and through the many nights following.

She knows that she will carry it with her forever.

Adventurer

HE LEFT HIS house at night. He is the only one to go, for the other children are under sixteen and father and mother are over forty-five. When he left, he called out by the door, "Bye! In three months I'll be back again!" He himself believed it, for such a war as this cannot go on for eternity, and if the Germans were not in such trouble they would not be taking the young Jews away here. They are afraid of the young Jews—that is the whole matter.

But at the same time he knew that father and mother did not believe the three months, otherwise mother would not have cried so and father would not have been so white. Three months is not worth crying over and being so white around your nose. It is because they are so old—then everything seems much worse to you.

He shut the door behind him, for in the darkened street they could not wave at him, anyway, and with large steps began the journey to the theater. The steps quickly became smaller because he has his thick winter coat and a knitted sweater over his shirt, since he cannot have all that in his rucksack. It is disagreeable, in the middle of the summer. The rucksack is big and heavy and then there are still shoes and rolled-up blankets over it. There are some good things in his rucksack, the best that mother had. And there are delicious things in his bread sack, things that they have not tasted for a long time; they are things from mother's supplies that she was saving for a rainy day—and for mother this is the rainy day. He does not know if he will have them for long, for when you have such tasty things with you and when you can be in charge of them yourself, then it is difficult to be sparing with your treats!

They take the rucksack from him. That is all right, he will get it back again. But they do not touch the bread sack. He does not mind passing his treats around among other boys, but nobody has to grab them if he is not there. If your are going to travel around the world, then you have to be careful.

He comes to the theater and is a bit disappointed with everything. There is the crying of children, and that always makes him nervous. You do not take a big adventure trip with little children. Oh, well, he does not have to babysit for them. Later when he is far away and he wants to launch an escape, he will do it together with other boys, and he will leave the people with little children behind. It is a shame that those people will not have a chance, but what can you do about it? It is miserable that they did not leave the children at home.

He has a fancy place on a red velvet seat. Secretly he must chuckle about it; the few times that he has been in a theater he had to sit in the gallery, for with that bit of pocket money it was not possible to sit lower down. He is sitting in the stalls now, and it is not costing him a cent! Only it is a shame that nothing is being played. There is an announcer there on the stage who has something to say through the loudspeaker all the time; he calls up people who must come behind the stage or to the hall or to the men in charge. He calls people who have lost something or who are being sought by their children. There is always something to call, and he would like the announcer to finally, finally keep his mouth shut. Never in his life has he heard *so* much noise without a moment of quiet; there is talking, shouting, quarreling, shuffling of feet, and incessantly, incessantly, there is the announcer calling.

When it is morning he wants to sleep, but he cannot, sitting straight up in his seat and among all those people. He will take something from his bread sack; they have already given him a few sandwiches, and he ate those long ago.

He really is in the mood for something tasty. He takes a bit of everything, wildly and greedily, because he himself is in charge of the food. But he does not rid himself of the sleepy feeling.

It has long been daytime as he hangs on his seat, with an aching back, his arms limp and his legs sinking away in front of him. Oh, how miserable he is—how miserable! Up until now he has been by himself when he has had to vomit. Oh no, but he does not want to vomit—not here with all those strange people! Only mother may be with him when he vomits—only mother, not strangers.

But it cannot be stopped. He cannot get by all the people in his row so quickly; he is bent over double on his seat, and he believes that he will die. His forehead is clammy with sweat, and then he hears a mill grinding instead of the racket that was all around him. He will be able to sleep now...

He notices that he is being picked up. Two people are holding his arms and legs and are carrying him somewhere, somewhere along steps. Good—that's good. At least the vomiting is over. Whatever else does not matter so very much to him.

As he lies on a sort of bed and a nurse washes the sweat from his forehead, he tries to smile reassuringly, but no one sees it. They leave him lying quietly, and that is all right with him because he is terribly sleepy. "I'm turning in," he mutters, as if he is talking with his brother; then he sleeps.

When he awakens and sees all the sick people around him, he knows it again. He sits erect.

"Nurse," he says, "I'm not sick!"

"All better?" nods the nurse.

"I wasn't sick," he says quickly. "Only a bit nauseated."

"That's lucky, fellow," says the nurse, "then another can lie down on your mattress."

He is a bit hurt by that "fellow" and wants to convince her that he really was not sick like all those others here.

"Miserable, all those sick people here, isn't it?" he says confidentially. "It's not for me."

And then, while he is hooking up his shoes that they had pulled off a while ago, he says, "You have to see it this way, nurse: they are letting us take a trip around the world, and it's not costing us a red cent!"

But the nurse pats him on the hair as if he were a child and says nothing.

Expensive Purchase

HER DEPORTATION SHOULD not have come about for a long time because she has a whole lot of good papers— and now they have taken her from the street in a roundup and here she is sitting in the theater!

She is not afraid. She is never afraid, of anyone or of anything. No one has ever been unfriendly to her, and no one will ever be unfriendly to her, either; she knows that for sure.

She also knows why there has never been anyone unfriendly to her. Because she is pretty. She is not blind when she looks into the mirror, is she? If you are pretty, you never have to be afraid of anything. Everyone will want to do what you ask—and she will ask to come out of here.

The man in green who shoved her into the police van—well, he had no time to see who was pretty and who was not. It was none other than a heap of people flung together in a corner of the street and then put into the van. He did not even count them; he merely seized those who were wearing a star and threw them on the heap. He did not see faces, either, and that really is such a shame, for otherwise she never would have turned up here. It was just as if he were afraid to look into their faces and to notice that they were people. He shouted throughout, perhaps out of the fear that he would think about what he was flinging onto the heap and shoving into the van.

But here, when she is a bit used to all that horror around her, she will calmly look at the men who make decisions about these things, and she will look for the most decent one and ask him to let her return home. She knows very well that the papers you have do not always help on a roundup day—but they will help *her*.

She looks about her. There is much crying. Some throng around a man who can get people out, even though he is Jewish. He puts both arms up to signal what he cannot say because they would not understand him amid all the noise: "I can't!" They hold him back and pull on his coat; they call to him, many voices at once, and thus he does not hear anyone correctly. Finally he wrings himself loose and escapes through a door that is forbidden to the others.

She will not join the throng with the others or shout with the others and not be understood, anyway. When she asks someone for freedom, she will do it alone and in such a way that the other shall see her face. It is nonsense to have a pretty face and not to use it.

She has enough composure to wait, enough sureness in herself not to grab the wrong chance. She does not allow the distress that is seen and heard all around her to penetrate her very much; her thoughts are directed only toward that *one:* to go free. Through that thought her sound little face remains unmoved, and there is no trembling around her blossoming mouth, not even when others speak to her and she absently answers them.

Then, when she has gone up the steps and the corridors and is back again, she sees a man in green, a man of importance, and she knows that he will be the one. She will not ask now because there are too many people in the area. She will stay in the corridor and wait for the moment.

When he is finally standing close to the window without people clawing all around him, she opens her purse where her papers are kept and goes toward him. She is now a bit anxious; she blushes and she speaks more quickly than she had planned when he asks her in German how he can be of service to her. Somewhat clumsily she takes out the papers; a little packet of vanilla sugar that she had just purchased when she was picked up, appears with them. Smiling, he takes it from her and asks her what it is.

"Oh, nothing," she says. "Vanilla sugar. I had just bought it."

"Come with me," he says, still smiling. "I must inspect that little packet."

She does not understand at all. The papers are what she would like him to see—and he wants to inspect the packet of vanilla sugar! Where is he taking her?

He goes in front of her, down the steps to an exit. When she has followed him through the door, they are in a dark little room, which is situated between this door and the door to the outside. There is only a small blue light burning. He puts the packet of vanilla sugar in the bag that she is still holding open in her hand.

"Is that all right?" he asks.

"I would like to be free," she says, her throat tight.

He takes a printed paper out of his pocket and signs it underneath the blue light.

"Would you like to have that?" he whispers. "They will not hold you any longer if you show them this."

Eagerly she reaches her hand out. But he takes the paper back and suddenly grasps her.

"First a kiss," he says hotly into her ear.

He kisses her, so terribly as never before a boy has kissed her. In that short moment she thinks about the other boys—four or five—who have kissed her. This—this is terrible.

Then suddenly he lets her go. He opens the outside door, and the blinding daylight comes inside. He takes the paper out again and puts it in her bag.

"This is freedom," he says. "It is well worth a kiss, isn't it?"

He disappears through the inside door, and she stands outside, dizzy.

She does not immediately know what she must do. Go home? Show the papers to everyone who wants to keep her there? And then what?

Her lips are burning. Everything that his hands or lips have touched is burning. She has not intended this. She wanted only to let him see her pretty face and through that have him allow her to go home. She did not know about this.

Oh, suddenly everything is changed! She will never again let herself be kissed by a boy—only by a man. When a boy kisses you, he looks, carefully. *He* found it immediately. When a boy kisses you, then he asks, astonished; *he* knew, always.

She can go home. But everything is changed, and it will never again be as it was previously.

She looks in her purse, which she has been holding open in her hand during all this time. Freedom is in it—and the packet of vanilla sugar. But all the rest that is not in her purse and that she suddenly realizes she possessed—all that is lost to her.

Youth.

Madonna

BY MORNING, AFTER a night of walking through the chilly, dark city, of arriving at the Star House, after a night of lying on a mattress amid the dust and noise, she noticed that her baby had become sick. She has it wrapped up in a blanket that was clean when she left home but that is now a dingy gray. She has gone to the sick ward and has shown it to the Jewish doctor.

Yes, the baby is very ill; it has a high fever, but the doctor does not know what the matter is. The baby must remain in the sick ward until tonight when the German officer, that mightiest power, will come to decide who is and who is not too ill to be shoved into the tram and sent on the journey. If the baby is found to be too ill to go, then the mother, who is herself a child, can also stay.

No, there is no bed for a child. Beds are for sick adults. The baby would take up only the head end, and to use a whole bed for that purpose is a shame. But the mother may stay in the sick ward even though she is not sick. She may go sit on a wooden bench with her back against the plastered wall and hold the baby in her arms. It is better for the baby there than in such a big bed, isn't it?

The hours go by as the mother sits erect against the white wall, her blue eyes wide open. The little bundle in her arms hardly moves; sometimes a small, plaintive sound comes out. Then she looks into the folded blanket and nods and smiles at what is inside, complaining and glowing hot. Then her arms rock back and forth gently until the little sound is silent.

She has let the baby drink from her breast a few times. She laid the little bundle down next to her on the bench in order to uncover her breast; then she took it up again and held it against her. The part of the little head that appeared out of the blanket was red and warm in contrast with her white breast. There was no support for her arm that was cradling the head; it is only a wooden bench on which she is sitting, and there are no arm rests on it.

The mother ate, too. Soup and bread were brought to her. She had one hand free to bring the spoon to her mouth; the other hand carried the baby. When the bowl was empty, it was taken away from her. Then she sat again with the baby in both arms and did not move.

It becomes evening and then night. The tension in the sick ward is unbearable. Soon, just before the Star House is emptied and the adults and children are driven into the departing trams, the mightiest power will come to look at and judge the sick. The doctors and the nurses know how much depends upon whether he is drunk or not.

Well, he is not drunk tonight. The good news is signaled upstairs before he reaches the sick ward. The assistants heave a sigh of relief.

Then suddenly he is standing in the middle of the sick. He asks questions, receives answers, but does not disclose his decisions.

The mother is sitting just as she has been for the whole day, without moving and with her blue eyes clear and wide open. The mightiest power stands facing her, big and well-fed and powerful. He sees her sitting quietly against the white wall, he sees her uncomplaining and unquestioning, and then shyly evades her gaze.

"How old is she?" he asks, turning his head to the side.

"Five months," says the Jewish doctor, and he takes the temperature of what is hidden there in the blanket.

"No—the mother."

The doctor bends over the mother and asks her how old she is.

"Nineteen."

The mightiest power shuffles his feet restlessly. He is still looking to the side.

"I have no time for all those cases tonight," he says hoarsely. "All the sick can remain behind."

The mother looks into the folded blanket and smiles.

Gift

THIS IS SOMETHING new, and everyone except the children themselves is happy about it: the children do not have to remain in the full Star House during all those twenty-four hours but will be taken across the street to a Jewish children's home where there are assistants, beds, gates, chairs, and lots of milk and porridge.

Relieved and yet anxious the mothers remain behind in the hell of the theater; but being in hell does not matter anymore now—at least the children are out! And tomorrow night when they are sent further on, they will get their children back—honestly they will!

The mothers reassure the crying children, kiss them, say goodbye to them for a whole day, and look somewhat gratefully and enviously at the assistants who go, each with a child in her arms, outside through the door that is closed to the mothers.

Life in the Star House continues, then, with all its gruesomeness, but without the children; the children will sleep in beds and tomorrow will play and be washed and fed. For one more day, just one, they will live as children are meant to live. After that...but then they will be together with their mothers, won't they? Then it does not matter anymore!

The daylight does not penetrate to the inside of the theater, but after the first night it came sparingly through the small windows in the corridors. That daylight is already gone again; the hours have crept by, and it is evening again. The ghost of departure is approaching; it will be greeted without reluctance because the other ghost that walks around in the Star House will be the victor. The journey cannot be more dreadful than this house. And what comes after the journey—oh, what difference does it make?

The mothers become restless. They are making themselves ready for the departure, and the children are not there yet. They will get the children back, won't they? They will not be taken away from them now, already?

Then comes the resounding of the announcer that all the mothers must come to the hall. A stifled cheer arises, a cheer such as this place has never heard before. This house has heard wailing and sighing and sobbing—and yes, even death rattles—but this sound is new.

The mothers stream into the hall. They look at each other, their eyes laughing, just like children who were promised a party. Their gazes are tensely directed upon the outside door, which is hidden behind a curtain.

The curtain is put aside, and the first assistant stands with a child in her arms. The mother rushes forward calling out "mine!" and reaches her arms out with the same gesture as her child does with his arms. The cry of the mother and of the child are also the same. The mother flees inside with her gift, as if she were afraid that her child could still be taken from her.

Again and again the curtain goes aside, again and again an assistant stands there with a child. Again and again a mother calls out "mine!" and flees back into hell with her regained treasure.

In half an hour they will be driven out. Where? It does not matter; they have their children back.

Joy—joy in hell. Or is perhaps the door left a bit ajar—the door that separates hell from heaven?

Missed Chance

IT HAS COME suddenly—but no, he is not really upset. So many of his comrades have already gone; why should he have more luck than the others? His papers had been giving him a postponement; now the roundup has come, and it has tossed that postponement right out the window. That is just, isn't it?

The roundup had been threatening to happen for several days, but no one knew just when it would burst forth. Too few were answering their summons to come to the theater. There were too many who were going into hiding at the last moment. And because the human harvest was too lean, the Germans had to come upon another method for filling up the places. Thus the roundup had to occur.

Well—now he is sitting here, and he cannot help that he is taking pleasure in the many who have gone into hiding. That is certainly worth a roundup. He is young and handy, and he will come through it all right. That other person who did not come to the theater on time because he went into hiding—perhaps that person would not have come through. He chuckles as he thinks how his comrades always teased him about his habit of looking at everything from the other side. It is a nice habit, for he is taking pleasure in it and is seeing only the unhappiness that is all around him.

"Hello!" calls out a hoarse, boyish voice. "So you're here, too?"

He turns around and sees the tight-lipped, cool face of a boy from his neighborhood.

"Hello!" he calls back. At least it is a boy, too. All those around him are men and women.

The other boy works his way through the people and looks for a place next to him. Now the two of them can have it good together.

"Have you already been to the front with your papers?" asks the other.

"Oh..." he shrugs his shoulders. "When it is my turn, they'll call me."

"You must keep at it!" advises the other sharply. "It won't happen by itself!"

A bit startled, he again notices that he is different from the others. It does not matter so much to him whether he gets out or not. What does a postponement mean? Soon all the Jews are going to be deported, anyway. And he does not want to go into hiding; he cannot play-act well enough, and he would be caught immediately. And always, always is that thought: another would go in my place, another who would not come through as well as I. The day passes. Many people are released. Perhaps they will still make allowances for those with papers? Oh, then they would certainly call him.

The police van keeps coming with new groups that are taken inside—and it is already late in the evening. This roundup is worse than the previous ones, which always stopped by evening. They will certainly not depart before tomorrow night. "Still chance enough," declares his conscience calmly, which opposes his passivity. "Still chance enough," he says soothingly to his neighbor, who does not understand his attitude.

Then out of the blue comes the chance. An assistant bends over them and whispers, "A group of sick people is immediately going to be sent away—released. Go stand there inconspicuously with them and walk with them. It won't be carefully checked."

Now his pulse is beating with excitement. My goodness, this is a chance to go home tonight and be able to tell all about it! He would still like to go home and lie in a bed tonight—and he would so terribly like to forget the others who must stay here and who will not be lying in a bed...

His neighbor is completely changed. The cool face is now glowing and shining.

"Come with me and hurry!" he says hoarsely. "Go stand among them and act sick!"

Acting sick is certainly something he cannot do. But perhaps it will not be necessary.

His heart is beating in his throat as he stands amid the sick in the corridor behind the outside door. He sees his friend putting on an act, his shoulders weak and hanging, his face twisted in pain. He *cannot* do that—oh, if he were to earn all the money in the world, he *cannot* do it! The outside door opens, and the night air comes to meet him, strange after all the stuffiness of the crammed theater. Suddenly he loves the night air and wants to do his best to forget about it.

Outside in the dark a biting German voice calls and commands for his papers permitting his release. He has none. He sees how his neighbor pulls a blank strip of paper out of his pocket and carelessly shows it to the officer and then walks through to freedom. And there he is himself, standing there with empty hands.

"Go back!" Shouts the voice. All right—he goes back again.

He sits again on his theater seat, this time without the boy next to him. He looks around him and sees misery and despair and is surprised that he can feel no sorrow for himself or for the chance that he missed.

No sorrow. Only an obstinate pleasure that for just a moment he breathed in the night air...

Comforting Milk

ALL THE MOTHERS have allowed their children to go across the street, but not this mother. For she herself may not go, and this child cannot be separated from its mother because no one else can feed it.

It does not matter that this infant remains in the theater and therefore must spend the twenty-four hours on a dirty mattress instead of in a crib. It does not matter that there is noise and shuffling of feet all around the child, which might prevent it from sleeping. As long as the child is with its mother it will not be lacking in happiness, for mother takes care of everything.

He who is there in the theater to offer his poor help,

to offer a single good moment where all good moments appear to be destroyed forever, comes to all the places at once, to all the stairs, into all the out-of-the-way places. He no longer hears any words but a buzzing; he no longer sees any faces but *one* moving, sorrowful blot. He must bend over a person and touch him in order to hear his words, to see his face, to feel his suffering rising up above the suffering of what buzzes and moves and fills the Star House up to the roof.

But again and again on his endless wanderings through the sorrowful jungle he meets this one mother. It is just as if she sits with her child in all places—and actually she has scarcely left her mattress. She has her child in her arms and is feeding it wherever you meet her.

Can a child drink *so* much milk? Will it never be satiated?

Oh, no, it hardly drinks at all. Perhaps it has drunk a few times during this whole night and day. It has otherwise sought only the warmth that radiates from the mother; it was enveloped by the cherishing of this mother's body; it slept and felt comfortable and did not know that a world was perishing around it.

He who is in the theater to offer his poor help must himself find a point from which to fetch help. While helping, he searches to see if there is any person in this heaving mass who has something to give.

Well—this mother has something to give. She is sitting and feeding her child, and her face is content and relaxed.

"Mustn't you yourself rest, mother? Close your eyes for a little while and lay your child down beside you and stretch out on the mattress? Hasn't the child had enough?"

The mother shakes her head with a smile. She does not expect to be understood, but she tries to answer the foolish questions.

"I'm not tired."

"But you will be tired—much too tired for what awaits you."

"Being tired isn't bad."

Then the mother feels pity for the face opposite her that does not seem to understand her language. She bends forward over the child, her face raised toward the one who reaches so high above her squatted posture on the mattress.

"I don't want my child to notice anything. I don't want my child to cry. Ever."

How high and powerful you can be, standing above what is squatting there! How high and powerful you can be, but in essence it is *you* who is kneeling down, small and poor, with an open hand raised for an alms—which is generously given to you...

Must

AMONG ALL THE adults and children streaming in there is only one with gray hair. That is grandfather. *Her* grandfather. The three of them have come together, mother and grandfather and she, and nothing bad can happen to her now.

She does not see that grandfather is the only one with gray hair. She does not know about age limits and about the older people who are still free to walk about. She knows only that they packed their rucksacks and took everything out of their house that mother thought was necessary and that they then closed the door behind them. They left nothing and no one behind. They brought the cat to the non-Jewish neighbors, who will certainly be as nice to it as they have been to it themselves. Those neighbors had wept bitterly when the three of them came to say goodbye. The man shook his fist; she knows very well at whom he did that, even though he did not say and she will not say, either, because you must not say anything out loud anymore. The woman picked her up as if she were still very small and kissed her. Oh, yes, she knows for sure that the neighbors will take good care of the cat.

After their rucksacks have been taken from them in the Star House, she walks further inside, safely between mother and grandfather. Now and again there is someone who points the way further to the places they will have until they go on their journey. It is very crowded and not as nice as she had thought it would be, but in between mother and grandfather it does not matter to her.

Each person who talks to them or points the way looks at grandfather a bit surprised. They are surely not used to such nice grandfathers. *She* is; she does not know how it would be without him. She is really a bit proud that they look at him so.

Then one who has also looked at him in surprise says, "But you don't have to be here! You are over the age limit!"

Grandfather shakes his head.

"I'm going voluntarily. I'm not letting my daughter and little granddaughter go alone."

The other nods and understands, better than she herself understands. Yes—that he is not letting mother and her go alone, that is not much to understand! That is a matter of course! But voluntarily...what is voluntarily?

As the three of them sit on three nice seats, with hers in the middle, she lays her little hand on grandfather's sleeve. He has just begun to look around at all those people and that bustle, but now he bows his white head to her.

"What is it, child?"

"Grandfather, what is voluntarily?"

He thinks about it a little.

"Voluntarily—that is, when you don't have to do something and you do it anyway."

She is quiet. Not have to? Did he not have to go and did he go anyway?

"But we had to, didn't we? Otherwise we wouldn't have gone, would we?"

"I didn't have to. Therefore I have gone voluntarily."

She really cannot understand it very well. But she is still a little girl.

"But you *had* to, grandfather! Otherwise you would have remained at home alone—and we couldn't have gone alone, could we?"

Grandfather takes her head between his hands and kisses her on her hair.

"That's why—that's why I had to go," he says. "That's why I had to go voluntarily."

Then she does not try anymore at all to understand what voluntarily means.

Island

OF ALL THE star children who were taken from the street in the roundup, there is not *one* as unhappy as she. She cries her eyes out, her splendid, dark eyes that you can hardly see behind the swollen eyelids, and yet new tears keep coming.

This *cannot* happen—married for two months and unable to be without him for a moment and then taken *alone*, without him! She may not reflect about it; therefore all she does is cry, just as she did when she was a little girl, for as long as she cries, she does not have to think.

"But perhaps something can still be done!" they say to her.

Something to be done? How can she do something

now, when he is not here? He always does everything, doesn't he?

"Now, now, your husband musn't see you like this!" teases an older man who has known her as a child.

"He won't see me anyway—he'll never see me again!" she cries.

She wants to tell everyone how miserable it is. The listeners shake their heads and forget their own lot for a moment. A few think, a bit enviously, how liberating it must feel to be able to cry *so* uninhibitedly. But for that you must be a child *and* married two months. Who has that privilege, to be a child and just married? Who else can scream out all the pain and fear, who else can let all the pain and fear flow away in tears?

Eat? No, no, she does not want to eat—she wants her husband back! Yes, and she also wants a clean handkerchief from the woman nearby who pats her on her shoulder and who forgets what she herself has left behind and what she herself must come up against. Papers, which could bring about her release? She does not know—honestly, she does not know. Her husband might have them. They may all look into her purse to see if there are papers there that could bring about her release. They may do what they wish. She will take out her wet handkerchief herself, as long as she does not have to look at the papers.

And so in this manner she lets herself flow away in the hours during which she sits there amid all the others; no one is angry at her because she is a child and just married.

Then an assistant comes to her, her face beaming. "If you promise to remain seated at your place, then I'll come to you right away, with someone."

She jumps up.

"Is he there? Has he come?"

"Yes. But remain seated, otherwise you'll never find each other."

Even before the assistant has left she wriggles by the people and escapes from her row. She cannot bear it. She must look for him herself. She pushes the others aside and tries to run. Her swollen little face spies to the left and right in order to find him quickly. But of course she does not find him.

She does find the assistant.

"Where is he? Where is he?" she asks, hurried and anxious.

"I can't bring you together this way!"says the other, shaking her head. "You were no longer at your place, and then I had to let him wait in order to look for you again. Now will you stay here?"

She speaks as if it were to a very small child, and the tear-stained little face seriously nods yes. But after she has stood waiting for a while, she believes that she may go to meet him, anyway. She pushes her way further through the sea of people.

How long is she wandering? It must be for a very long time; she has gone quite far. Pushed by the stream that seems to have no destination and no end, she has reached the stairs. Then suddenly there is a pair of arms around her and a mouth on her mouth, which smothers her cry of delight.

The words are all foolish ones that she hears and that she whispers back. She only kisses him and cries and lets herself be soothed, and she does not know at all where she is anymore.

"Are you silly?" she hears him whisper into her ear. "Do you think that I would let you go alone? If we come free, then we'll come free together, and if we must go, then we'll go together. Away together, home together. What do you say?"

They stand there in the middle of the steps, kissing each other. The whirlpool of people that goes up and down is resigned and bends around this island of happiness. But they do not know that a whirlpool exists there and that they have formed an island in it—for they are filling the whole world.

Secret

SHE HAS SEEN it—she *herself* has seen it happen—and it is too awful to be able to tell to father and mother. *That* is the worst thing.

She knows that she will never be able to forget the face of that old man. She had seen him several times before in the few days that they have been here in the theater; she thought that he had such a nice, kind-hearted face, only it was a very sad one. But there are so many people in the theater going around with sad faces. Perhaps she is too, certainly now that this has happened and that she cannot tell father and mother.

That he is dead now—for of course he is dead—that is not so terrible. He would be happy about that. But that it *happened* and that she *saw* it...

She was in the highest corridor of the theater, alone among all the strangers. She had been away more often from father and mother and her brother during those few days. You cannot stand it when you are sitting at the same place all the time; then you become touchy with your brother or tearful with father and mother, just when you would like to be good. The best thing to do, then, is to walk up the stairs, one foot at a time, because you cannot do it any other way among all those people; otherwise how she would like to run and slide back down the banister, just as she used to do at home! She goes through the corridors, all the way to the top, and then comes down again. Sometimes she meets children she knows from school. That is a lot of fun, of course, even though it lasts for just a moment, for those children must also return to their parents and to their own places, and it is not so easy to find them again. Then when she is back again with father and mother, everything seems much newer and not so difficult anymore.

She met him a few times on those trips. He did not talk to anyone, and he had no one with him, no one who belonged with him. Perhaps that was it. She knows now that she wondered a few times whether or not she should have said "grandpa" to him in passing; she said that once to another older gentleman, and a smile lit up his whole face. But she did not say it to him—did not dare, perhaps—and now she must think again and again that perhaps it would not have happened if she had only dared to say that one word "grandpa" to him. Because she saw it happen, she believes that it must have been a little bit her fault.

The window of that corridor was open because it was so stuffy in the theater and because in an hour, by dark, everything had to be completely closed anyway, for the blackout. There were only a few people standing close to the window—luckily she was not one of them.

Then she saw him among the people. It was just as if he had become blind and could no longer see, or as if he were sleeping and yet could walk. She knows now with complete certainty that she saw that first, before it happened; she did not think it up later. And then it happened *so* quickly that she heard the people way down below in the street shriek before she could give a scream herself. He pushed aside the people who were standing in front of the window, very strongly, as if he were suddenly no longer an old man—and then she did not see him anymore. Then she heard the screams of many people in the street, and she herself screamed and the others in the corridor, too, who thronged toward the window to look out. But one big, calm man pushed them aside and closed the window. Then a few men in green uniforms came storming upstairs, and they shouted at the people that no one could come to the window and what were they doing there and that not a single window in the theater could be open, ever again.

Then she became so nauseated and dizzy but she could not be sick—not here and certainly not with father and mother, for she could never tell it to them. She never can tell it to them—never. Perhaps they will hear about what has happened from others, and they will certainly not tell her brother because it is too nasty for children to hear. How can she say to them, then, that she has seen it! How in the world can she ever tell anyone about it?

Mother feels that she must try to sleep sitting up, for she looks so white. She is white from nausea, of course. But how can she sleep now? All the time she sees the face of the old man in front of her, so blind, so sleeping. She should have said "grandpa" to him each time that he went past her. If you have a girl who says "grandpa" to you, you are unable to do that horrible thing. It is a bit her fault. Now he is dead and is happy to be dead. But that he is happy about it...oh, how can she bear it if she cannot tell anyone...

Then she says to her brother, "Say, if people fall out of a window, very high, would they be dead when they got to the bottom?"

"Crazy!" he says, and he laughs, just as boys laugh when they talk about silly girls.

Mother asks what it was about; she is afraid of bickering between her brother and her, for that has already happened a few times during these days.

"She's asking me if you're dead when you fall out above from the window!" he sniggers.

Then mother becomes very angry at her.

"Must you listen to nasty stories that the people here make up?" she says.

She does not answer. She knows that mother has already heard about it. Now she will *certainly* never be able to tell it—never.

But because mother is speaking angrily to her, suddenly she can cry. Slow, warm tears, that hurt her throat but that make everything different. Different and better.

Trust

FOR THE WHOLE day they have been sitting next to each other or lying on the mattress, the two little sisters. What the biggest one has said, the littlest one has echoed, at least those words that she could say. They are wearing identical warm outfits with long pants; mother made them a long time ago so that they would be ready for the journey, which surely would come one day. Their dark curls lie with the same waves on the clear foreheads and the sound little cheeks. Their velvety eyes look with the same trusting devotion from under the long, black lashes.

They have often been alone today. Last night when they had arrived from the dark street, mother had lain down with them on the mattress. She had pulled the warm suits off and had laid a blanket over them. They slept and were very content, for mother was with them. Father sat somewhere else on a chair, for men do not get a mattress.

But the next morning father came to show mother how swollen his one leg was becoming. It had been swollen for a week, but he could still get a shoe from a neighbor on because that neighbor has big feet. Now father has stumbled to them without a shoe, for his foot has become *so* swollen that he had to take the shoe off.

"You have fever," mother said to father. Mother can always feel it immediately if you are sick. "Come with me."

Then mother said to the biggest sister that she must be good and stay on the mattress and watch over the little sister. The older girl nodded yes, and whenever she nods yes, she always remembers it and does it.

Now father is in the sick ward with his foot on his rucksack and with wet cloths wrapped around it. Mother can leave him, for the nurses are taking care that nothing happens to his foot, but mother must continually be with the men in charge to ask if father can go to the hospital and if the three of them can go home.

When mother is not there, the other mothers look to see how the two sisters are doing. They also give them their meal that the little girls obediently eat, although they would much rather wait with food until mother is back. But they do not want to sleep, so they sit erect, next to each other on the mattress, and they look at the entrance to see if mother is coming.

Sometimes mother is there for a short while; she then squats next to the girls and eats something because the other mothers would be angry with her if she did not. She wipes their little faces with the wet washcloth that she has brought with her in a little bag, and she has them go to the bathroom—she has brought all the necessary things with her—and then she is gone again. But those short moments are not the ones in which the horrible things happen that make the little sisters afraid. They are not the moments in which the nasty soldiers in green uniform come to the mothers and children and shout things with such loud voices, things that they do not understand. They are the same kind of soldiers as those who let them inside this house; at the time mother said that the soldiers would not harm anyone, and perhaps that is so, but still it would have been nicer if mother had by chance been with them when the soldiers approached them.

When the soldiers are away again, the little sisters sit straight as an arrow on their mattress; they hold each other by the hand, and the biggest says slowly, with a deep voice that seems to come out of her sleep, "The soldiers are *not* bad!"

The littlest sister nods with large, serious eyes.

"Not-ad," she says.

When it is dark, mother comes again for a moment and lays them down to sleep. She says that they should sleep for a while; the men do not yet know whether father may go to the hospital and whether they may return home. If they must go away, then mother will awaken and dress them.

Obediently they lie next to each other under the blanket and fall asleep. Mother speaks with the Jewish doctor and with other men who are knowledgeable of what is and is not permitted in the Star House, and at the last moment they are still afraid that father's leg is not painful enough and that his fever is not high enough; mother then awakens the little sisters and rolls up the blanket and dresses the children.

They sit next to each other, drunk with sleep and stiff from the thick clothes that mother has put on them. They do not understand it so very well, but the oldest sister knows that it has something to do with those soldiers.

"The soldiers are *not* bad," she says.

The littlest sister nods, "Not-ad."

But in the sick ward the nurses are trying to bind father's leg and then to get a stocking or at least a shoe on, but they cannot. He is in terrible pain and is doing his best to bear it. But the shoe really cannot go over his foot. The doctor then believes that he can remain and that early the next day, after six, he can be brought to the hospital. Without a shoe he cannot begin the long journey, can he?

Again mother goes to the sisters. All the mothers are busy packing and dressing children, and in the midst of the turmoil she undresses the little girls again. She brings them to a corner in the corridor that is now empty and where there is a mattress on the floor. She tucks them in again and kisses them goodnight. The little sisters were really not yet awake, and they immediately go back to sleep.

But the German officer who is the mightiest power comes, drunk. He storms into the sick ward and rages at the many sick people who are naturally trying to trick him. He threatens the Jewish doctors with death because they are keeping so many Jews back. The Jewish doctors know this; they have long since overcome the fear of death, and they point to the sick who really cannot go.

"All those with temperatures below 104° can travel," he roars. "And they'll be checked."

But the father of the little sisters cannot get a shoe on his swollen foot.

"So What! It's dry weather—he can go without a shoe!"

Mother awakens the little girls in the now quiet corner of the corridor. They cannot wake up, and mother must make the washcloths soaking wet from the water in the sick ward and wash their faces in order to bring them back to life.

They do not understand. They stand wobbling on their little legs and let themselves be wrapped up in many clothes by mother's hurried fingers. Then the biggest sister understands that it might have something to do with the soldiers again.

"The soldiers are *not* bad," she says.

The littlest sister nods and still sleeping, stammers, "Not-ad."

The Younger

THE BIG BROTHER and his young wife and he, the younger brother, had thought that it would be so different. It was a few years ago, even before the big brother had thought about a girl, that they knew for sure: when they were finished with their vocational training, they would go together to Palestine. Perhaps the older brother would not wait for the younger one, for he could make a place ready for him in the meantime, couldn't he? But that they would go, that was the certainty that the young woman later shared with them.

Everything has come too late. In the beginning of the occupation when they did not yet know what it would mean later on, they calmly went on with their work, which was directed toward going to Palestine. There would come a time after this time, and in the meanwhile they would have finished their studies. And yet—and yet...

If the three of them are going to be deported then there *must* be a way out over there, sooner or later. They *will* find it; they will help each other to find it. Last night they said goodbye to father and mother, who have not yet been sent away, and they were able to leave some of this certainty behind with them.

They go through all the formalities and registrations together; they bear the same name that begins with the same letter of the alphabet, and that makes everything easier. The older brother completes it all; but in the narrow face of the younger boy, a face that is actually still a child's face, the lips are pressed together in determination, and he has the feeling that he himself is doing what must be done.

The older one sits in the middle. When his wife leans her head sleepily on his shoulder, the brothers look at each other and smile. They are the men.

Throughout the whole night and the whole next day the loudspeaker resounds above their heads. They scarcely hear it anymore, until their name is called—the name of the older brother and his wife. They must go through the drafty fire exit to the area behind the stage. On the stage the game of chance is played to see who must go and who may remain behind.

"See you later," he says to his younger brother. "Don't come. We'll take care of it for you."

After a while he sees them from his seat, coming on stage like tiny actors, behind many others. The play drags; it takes a long time before he ses them talking with those who are sitting and writing there behind the little wooden table.

Something is not right. He watches them just as a tense viewer watches a play that knows to hold its public with special effects. He sees how papers are produced and how "no" is signaled with the shake of a head. He is much too involved in it to think about what it can mean; he merely waits, his heart pounding, for the return of those who belong with him. Then he sees them leaving the stage with heads bowed.

He still does not know as they stand before him.

"We two are free," says the older one dully.

We two? Which two? Which two belong together? Then he understands. The man and wife—they are a family. Not the big brother and he, the younger.

"Now that is lucky for you," he says glibly, like a formula. He does not know what else to say. He sees that his brother is very white and that his mouth is twitching. God, don't let him cry, for then everything is lost!

"See you in Palestine then—OK?" he hears himself say.

The brother nods, his white face in control again.

"If you still want us to go with you—voluntarily..."

"Are you *crazy?*" the words slip out violently. "I can go alone."

After the young woman has packed up their possessions, the big brother kisses the younger one on the forehead. The sister-in-law kisses him, too. Then they are gone.

They should not have done that, they should not have kissed him. For when they are no longer in view, the taut thread breaks in him.

"Mother!" he screams.

New Mother

SHE VENTURED OUT of the house today for the first time to buy some things that she could no longer do without. There is no one at home with the baby; her husband will not come home from work until tonight, for now that he may no longer go by bicycle or by tram, he is unable to come home at lunch time.

She did not know that there would be a roundup today, otherwise she would have stayed at home. When she was returning home from the store with her purchases in her shopping bag, she suddenly came upon two men in green uniforms who pushed her toward a crowd of other Jews and brought them in a police van to the theater. Everything happened *so* quickly that she did not immediately understand what was going on. Now there is just one thing about which she can think: that her baby is alone in the house and that soon it will be two o'clock and she will not be there to feed it. Tonight her husband will come home and discover that she is not there; in what condition will he find the baby, who already will have missed two feedings and who perhaps will never get its mother back?

The baby was born only two-and-one-half weeks ago. It is so small that it looks as if it had been born yesterday, and it cries a lot. Surely it will die, now that it is alone in the house and is not being fed. Perhaps it is better if the baby dies, for it is a star child, and it will have to cry much more than it has up until now. But for nine months the mother looked forward to it, and it took many hours for the baby to push its way out into the world; she would so have liked to have kept it and to have seen it grow big and to have heard it say "mother." That is not *so* much to ask, is it, when you waited for the child for nine months and in terrible pain gave birth to it? Surely that must not have all been for nothing! When the dullness recedes, she stands up from her seat and looks for someone who perhaps can help her. She sees an assistant going by, one who is older than she and who looks like a mother. She speaks in a monotone, as if she were reciting a lesson.

"My baby is two-and-one-half weeks old. This morning I left home for the first time, and they caught me. There is no one at home. At two o'clock I must feed it."

She does not ask the woman to help her. She does not cry. She merely sums up what has happened.

The woman is a mother herself. She *sees* the baby in the empty house, and she knows that she will never again in her life have any peace of mind if she is unable to have this new mother sent home. And so the long wandering of the old woman and the very young one begins, through the theater, past all the many who would like to help but do not have the power to do so.

Finally the older woman puts her question before a man in uniform who does have the power. The question is a command, an urgent command. And then the power of the little baby in the empty house reaches out to what is there enveloped in a green uniform with silver stripes. He listens to the thin, newborn sound of a hungry little person in a distant street.

"Yes," he says. "She can go."

When the young mother has the paper in her shopping bag, the paper that would conduct her safely through her search, the older woman brings her to the exit. And there where the daylight is coming through, she suddenly becomes the tender and weak new mother that she actually still is. She lays her head against the shoulder of the other and cries.

"God bless you and your work," she sobs.

"Don't cry," says the older woman, feeling foolish and helpless. "Your child mustn't drink any tears."

Outside in the emptied street that is burning in the sunlight, she feels the milk flowing to her breasts. She runs home, driven forth by what she has left behind in the Star House—drawn forth by what is thirstily awaiting her.

Operation

THE BOY, HIS father, and mother were not in the theater for even two hours when the woman began having pain. She wanted to stifle it at first, especially for her two men, the little one and the big one; they cannot bear that she is sick. But when she could no longer suppress it, she told them and, frightened, they took her up the many steps to the sick ward. A long line of sick people stood outside the door, waiting until the doctor could help them, but when the pain became very bad, they brought her in sooner.

Now the father and the boy are waiting behind the line of sick people in front of the door. They do not dare to speak to each other. The father does not want to share his fear with an eleven-year-old child, thus he merely hums to himself; the boy believes that father does not half know how sick she is, and thus he prefers to let father be deluded into thinking that the illness will soon pass and that he may as well keep humming. He cannot recall mother ever being sick, and that makes it much worse.

The two of them no longer know why they are here in the theater. The departure from home, so thoroughly prepared with clothes and supplies, is long forgotten. The journey to the distance that is vague and unknown recedes into a veiled future. Reality is mother who is in pain and who is hidden there behind that door.

Whenever the door opens to let in the next sick person, both of them stretch to see what is happening there behind it. The father tries to question the nurse standing by the door, but she says that he will soon hear, after mother is examined; it is not her turn yet.

Finally the doctor himself comes to the door and calls the name of the father. The boy comes forward with him and looks fearfully at the man in the white coat who is making the decision over mother. The doctor, a surgeon, is beaming with professional zeal. He says that it is very acute—just the right time to operate.

"Tonight, after all the people have left, I will have her brought to the hospital, and I will operate on her," he says.

The father nods. He lets himself be taken in by the visible enthusiasm of the doctor, and suddenly he comprehends what it means: a postponement for the three of them—to remain and then wait and see. But the boy has heard only the word "operation." Operate and hospital. Violently he grabs the doctor's white sleeve and cries in a high, frightened voice, "Doctor, doctor—is that dangerous? Is she going to die?"

The doctor laughs as loudly as is scarcely permissible at the entrance of a sick ward in a star house.

"Be happy, boy! It couldn't have come at a better time! Tomorrow after six you can go home!"

The boy lets go of the doctor's sleeve as if it has burned him. Be happy—with mother's pain! It couldn't have come at a better time, mother's pain...

He turns around and crying, pushes his way through the thronging mass.

Unloading

EVER SINCE FATHER and mother had been sent away together with the other children, she has been longing to be taken herself, really. She, the eldest, was allowed to stay behind because she belonged to a group of students who did not have to go. But she had wanted to go with the others, even then. Father and mother did not want it, however; they said that you should not go a minute sooner than you had to. Obediently she remained behind and lived with strangers. Now that she has been taken, she has the feeling that finally she is being allowed to follow the others.

Being in the theater is merely a wait for her departure. She is not impatient—oh, no, she will undergo the series of events just as the others have already done. She faces her own lot blankly, since she had to give up the only arbitrary interference—to go with the others. For herself she is calm.

But in the course of the long day an uneasiness grows

in her, oppressing, dominating. She is uneasy because of what she sees around her and for what she sees through the eyes of father and mother. They were here and were worried about the younger children; they were hurt by the violence around them; they were fearful about what further would happen, especially to the children; they felt great sorrow about what they had left behind, mother's family, father's work that he had built up himself. Her parents left this place, but their dark thoughts are still wandering around here, and they oppress this child, who did not have to have any dark thoughts about herself.

In this oppressiveness she is open, too open, to what the people around her are undergoing; she is more sensitive to the older people than to those her own age. By evening, when the people are gathering their possessions and are excited and hurried, or dull and defeated, a rebelliousness against this humiliation and injustice is growing in her such as she never knew before in those months of increased oppression. She herself has few possessions to collect; she has taken only a few things with her because she did not want to be heavily laden and because she can get along with very little. But she sees the loads that the mothers of large families have to look after, and again she thinks about what father and mother had to pack and what they left behind.

Then the exodus begins. The men in green are shouting and driving the people on; they are in such a hurry, as if something horrible is persecuting them, and yet *they* are the ones who are persecuting. Perhaps they do not know that they are persecuting, perhaps they believe that they are being persecuted.

She is standing upright with her light load, and she sees the bent backs of the others that seem to be folded double under whatever is left of their previous possessions. The rebelliousness has not been softened now that the end of the wait has come. Perhaps if all those bent backs were not going out in front of her, she could have felt a sense of liberation.

Then she sees a man in green uniform, big and coarse, who is giving a small, heavily laden Jew a shove in order to hurry him along. The man can hardly keep his balance. And then a whirlwind goes through her that prevents her from thinking clearly.

"Leave him alone!" she shouts to him in German. "Leave him alone!"

The giant turns toward her. His face is so distorted from anger that it no longer appears human. He raises his fist to hit her and without a sound he hisses, "What! What!"

In this one very clear moment she knows that this is the end. When the fist falls, then everything is over. She does not care. She stands very straight and looks at him.

And then, strangely and unexpectedly, it is not yet all over. The fist is lowered, without hitting. She breaks loose from the spell of waiting for the end, turns her gaze away from that face that is no longer a face, and walks further to the exit. But the man in green pushes through the stream of those being driven out and goes after her, raging.

"One more word and you'll see what happens!" he shouts.

She knows that she should keep walking, but she cannot. She no longer has any feeling for safety and danger; she must turn around and look at him and say the one word about which he warned her; the one word in which she unconsciously discloses what she expected when she called to him to leave the man alone; the one word of a disillusioned child who today has ceased to be a child: "I thought that you were a human being."

Then others seize her and push her to the exit to safety.

In the dark crowd surrounding the tram she realizes that her cry, her useless cry at what was no longer a human being, has liberated her.

She breathes deeply and lets herself be pushed into the tram.

Peddling in the Dark

DURING THE TIME when the stream of people was driven outside, the one assistant, who was needed elsewhere, shoved a little basket into the hands of the other assistant. In the basket lies a very small baby, whose name was hastily called out in the transfer. Now this other assistant must go into the dark street to find its parents. Perhaps they have already reached a tram that has ridden away; then the baby will never find them again.

She walks with the little basket to the other side of the rails, calling out the name that was told to her. The burdened Jews who go past her need to give all their attention to their own families, their own loads, their own way to the trams that will carry them off. They do not hear her. She remains standing on the other side, close to the tram that will presently become full and then ride away. She calls out the name of the baby as a cry of distress.

When the basket becomes too heavy and she can no longer stand, she sets it down on the dry street and squats next to it. She keeps calling. In the dim blue light of the tram she looks hopefully at each young couple going inside; she calls somewhat louder, then—perhaps they are the ones.

Her monotonous call is like a prayer.

"God, hear how I am offering this child for sale in the dark street! Hear how I must call out for the father and mother, who perhaps have already been sent off! God, look down upon this child and this street and these trams and remember it for all eternity! Let this baby who has been mislaid from its father and mother remain before you, until you have brought punishment upon those who have committed all this! God, hear all of this and see all of this and do not forget it!"

She does not know how long she is squatting down there, or how long she is shouting out the name of the child and calling to God. She turns away from God, toward herself.

"If I do not find the father and mother, I will keep the baby. A little baby for myself. My children are grown, and already one of them has been dragged away toward the unknown. May I keep this one small baby for myself if it does not find its father and mother again?"

Then she is frightened and turns away from herself, toward God. But her voice calls only the name of the baby while new trams keep filling and riding away.

"God, forgive me, that I have desired this baby! Let it find its father and mother again! Forgive me, God, forgive me!"

Behind her, out of the dark, comes a voice of a young man.

"Thank God!"

A man and a woman kneel down by the little basket and sob and grab each other by the hand. Then the assistant knows that it is their baby and that God has forgiven her and that perhaps He has also heard her prayer to see all of this and not to forget it.

The two whisper together. They have gone through the fear of loss during these fifteen minutes—or was it longer? Or was it shorter? Now that the fear is past, they wonder if they should leave the baby behind with its grandmother, who may remain for the time being. They must decide quickly, for the last trams are ready to depart.

"Come on," says the man suddenly and picks up the little basket, "let the three of us be done in together."

The older woman stands watching them as the trams ride away, and her arms feel strangely listless and empty.

The Curtain Falls

THE ROUNDUP DAY is at an end; now it is night, and no new arrivals of Jews will be coming.

On the stage the men in green uniforms and the Jewish assistants have worked together in unison in the registration and selection of those who can and who can not return to freedom. The announcer has called out the names of those who had to come up on stage and join the play.

It is a new thought in the area of theater, to put the administration of a wholesale trade on stage and to display the merchandise through living beings. An entertainer with a loudspeaker is also new and original. Professionally it really is quite nice. It could be an undisputed success if it were not for that one fault, that one unforgivable fault: it is too long and too monotonous. The play is moving enough, since it is taken from real life, but it is always the same—*always* the same. Even the most patient public cannot remain at close attention. And this public *is* patient, for it endures more than was ever thought to be possible.

Now it is night, and the actors behind the administration table feel that it is getting to be too long. They, the men in green uniforms and the Jewish assistants, are themselves tired. The light in the auditorium has already been dimmed until only the blue lights remain on. Those sitting in the audience have positioned themselves in such a way that they are ready for sleep. Why will the actors play even longer? To free more Jews? A line must be drawn somewhere, mustn't it? Those whose turns have come have had good luck—the others were not so fortunate.

The entertainer withdraws and dims the lights on the stage, also. The other players gather their papers and disappear into the wings.

Then the fire curtain falls. The corrugated iron descends slowly and brings the separation between the auditorium and the stage. It will not go up tomorrow, for the rest of the piece will be played in the auditorium. That is also new and original, to draw the public into the play. But if it becomes too long again—too long and monotonous...

The curtain is down. Intermission.

3. Star Desert

Caravan

TODAY HAS BEEN a very long day; it began early, and it seems like it will never end. It is *so* long and so many strange things are happening that he is sleeping while walking at father's hand instead of looking around and noticing *how many* strange things are happening.

He awoke this morning when it was actually still night. That normally never happens to him, but a car came through the street, and a man who was sitting inside was beeping something very loudly through the loud-speaker. Father and mother went to the window to listen to what that man was saying, but he himself was still too sleepy to get out of bed. When the man was finished speaking, he waited a bit and then said something again, a little further down the street. He could hear from the last sentence that it was the same thing that he had said just before. And when the man called it out for the third time, he understood it all. He was not even frightened because he had heard it one and one-half times already.

All Jews had to remain in their homes and get their baggage ready. The non-Jews could go out on the street only to go to work; otherwise no one could go out on the street. That was approximately what he heard.

"Shall we get up, then?" he asked father and mother.

Startled, they turned toward him. They had not thought that he was awake and that he had heard everything—he, the eldest.

"Did you hear it?"

"The third time."

Then mother came and sat on the edge of his bed and stroked him. She usually does that only to the little ones; he is too big for such things, but today he finds it a very pleasant thing for her to do. She looks above him at the little portraits that are hanging on the wall and says, "It's come." Father comes and stands next to mother and lays his hand on her shoulder. "We have had it good, all those years," he says. And he himself is very, very happy that he is the eldest and that he was awake when the message was called out and that father and mother are so nice to each other and to him and that they have had it good all those years.

Then father and mother quietly get to work; they do not want to awaken the two little ones and the baby, and they want him to sleep some more, for a lot will be happening today. He closes his eyes for a while, but he sees through his eyelashes how father and mother return through the open door to their own bedroom, where the cradle and the baby's table are, and how mother takes out the diapers and baby clothes and how father takes out many other things from the linen closet. He tries to remain lying down for another five minutes, but then he thinks about everything that is not in his rucksack yet, things that he has needed every day and that he still wants to take with him. He really cannot remain lying down; the voice coming from the car did not say what time they would be coming to get them, thus it could be soon enough. He slides out of bed quietly—the little ones musn't wake up—and he begins to dress. Mother comes to him right away.

"Wait a minute, darling," she says. Normally she never calls him darling, for he is a boy. "Wait a minute and I'll give you more underwear. Then we won't have to carry it."

It is a warm day, but still he puts on all the double layers of underwear that mother gives him. He does not complain. The more he puts on, the more room there will be in his rucksack for the things that he would like to put in.

Then the little ones awaken and the baby, too. They are all thickly clothed, and they must eat a lot, as well, for father and mother do not know when they will be able to eat again. The little ones do their best; it is a long time ago since they were allowed to eat as much as they wanted, thus it is not so very difficult to eat more than at other times.

When mother wants to wash the breakfast dishes, father laughs at her as if he were a naughty boy.

"Are you silly?" he calls. "For whom must we leave it clean? Children, you may make as much mess as you want!"

"Clippings too? Everywhere?" asks the little sister.

Father picks her up and shakes her to and fro above his head.

"Clippings, too. Everywhere."

The little ones industriously set themselves to mess making and he, the eldest, joins them after he has packed his rucksack with the things he wants to take with him. It takes hold of him, the strange game of mess making. He almost forgets what the man in the car called out this morning and what is going to happen today. He forgets that they are in their own rooms with their own things for the last time and that they actually should be sad. Clippings and old rags and pieces of newspaper are lying about everywhere now. The little ones are having a marvelous time, and he is, too. At a moment when the little children are still earnestly and industriously at work, he stands erect with his hands in his pockets and sighs with satisfaction.

"What a holy mess!" he says admiringly.

His sister looks up, wrinkles her brows, and says with a respectable, careful little mouth, "Oh, father, he's saying 'holy mess'! You mustn't say that, right, father?"

And then, with a glance at the growing mess, she

adds, "But we're *sitting* in what he says, aren't we, father?"

The moment comes when the doorbell is rung very loudly. They know what it is, for neither Jew nor non-Jew will be coming to their door today.

It is two men in green uniform. They count the adults and children, ask for their papers, and shout that they must be ready in five minutes. If it takes longer, they will throw their belongings down the steps, they say; it will come down the steps more quickly that way. They shout everything that they have to say; they cannot do otherwise.

Everyone except the baby is carrying a rucksack, and mother pushes the baby carriage upon which the baby's name and birthdate are painted, and father and he carry the cradle between them. It is full of diapers and baby clothes, but father carries yet another heavy suitcase. All their Jewish neighbors and acquaintances are together in the street and are heavily laden. They do not say anything but merely look at each other and say with their eyes what they may not say with their mouths. You hear only the shouting of the men in green and a few children who are crying softly.

The people are put in a tram. The rucksacks and suitcases remain in the street; they will be forwarded to them, if their names are on them, that is. The baby carriage remains behind, too. The baby is now lying on her own clothes in the cradle that father and mother have set down between them on the seat of the tram. It is very funny to be sitting in a tram again; how long has riding a tram been forbidden to Jews?

There are many non-Jews standing along the route of the tram, for it is time for them to go to work. Most of them take their hats off and weep. He has hardly ever seen big men crying, and he finds it rather eerie that they are crying over him and the other Jews. The Jews themselves are not crying. They are quiet and are merely looking about. The men in green are shouting. When he thinks about it, that the Jews are the only ones who are not cry-

128

ing or shouting and that it is to the Jews that all this is happening, he has to laugh to himself. Funny.

After they step out of the tram they are shouted at and shoved together onto a large square. In the building that formerly was the shul there are people writing, and there father must give all their names and hand over their house key. Thus they have nothing more than their suitcases and rucksacks that are lying somewhere in the street and that perhaps will be sent to them.

They stay as close together as possible. When a new tram comes again and thus more people must be held in the square, then the men in green shout a bit louder and herd them closer together. Right next to him sits a very old man who has no one with him and who is sitting on a crate because he is so tired. But the old man cannot remain seated when they have to move in. Again and again he says, "Come, I'm going home; I don't live here." Surely he does not understand that he no longer has a home and that he no longer lives anywhere. When you are that old, you do not understand things very well.

It actually was made very easy for them. They were brought to the station in a tram. They did stand at the station for hours in the sun, with their thick, double layers of clothing on, and in the midst of the bustle mother had to set the cradle with the baby and the clothes down on the ground and had to let the baby drink—but at last the train came, and it was not even a cattle train. He cannot help that he finds it wonderful to sit in a train and to travel, just as if they were no longer Jews to whom everything is forbidden. Only it is a shame that it is so warm and that the windows are not allowed open. A few people did not understand that the windows absolutely must not be opened, and when the train stood still at a station, the men in green cursed and shouted and aimed their guns at the open windows. Then the windows were quickly slammed shut, and fortunately the train rode on before the men in green had shot at them. He was badly frightened by those guns, but luckily the little ones did not see them.

They have stepped out of the train now. It is almost dark, and it is a bit chilly. He cannot see where they are walking but lets himself be pushed along in that long line of people. Actually, he is sleeping.

In front of him are the backs of people, and behind him are feet shuffling forward, which would walk over him if he did not move along with father. The cradle with the baby inside is set outside the line. Mother is sitting at the foot-end, and the little ones are leaning against her. There is room for mother at the foot-end because the baby's legs do not reach that far. Each time the line moves forward because a group of people has been let inside a little wooden house where everything is written down, then he and father leave the line and together lift the cradle and carry it forward, too. Then mother can go sit down again and the little children can again lean against her. And he can go stand at father's hand again and sleep some more.

It has become completely dark, and it has begun to drizzle. Through his many clothes he can still feel the cold of the night. Mother has laid a thick woolen cloth over the baby's face; a small hole must remain open, otherwise it would be too stuffy for her. The baby cries a little now and then. The little ones do not; they are too sleepy to cry. But there are other children in line who do cry, and when they do they are scolded by their fathers or mothers or by people who are standing around them who cannot endure crying.

As if those little children can help it that they have to cry!

It seems to him that it is in the middle of the night when they are pushed somewhere inside. There are people with stars on who ask father everything and who write it all down. Luckily they are friendly. He is glad that they are people with stars and not men in green uniforms. He is not afraid of the men in green, but they always shout so.

Then they stand outside again, and in the dark they are taken somewhere else. Again they wait in line and then come inside again, and at last they come to a man in green, who examines all their pockets and all their clothes to see if they still have money or anything else that should have been turned over in that other little house. Then they come to a doctor and nurses in white coats, and they must undress. He goes with father and the little children with mother, and they all have their hair and their throats examined. And then *again* they stand in line outside. Day is beginning to dawn, and it is very cold and wet. Just when he thinks that they will never again, *never* again be allowed to sit or lie down or sleep, he and mother and the little ones and the baby are let into a long wooden shed called a barrack. Father is sent to the other half, and he says "good night" before he leaves them. Because of that he understands that perhaps they may sleep.

There in the semidarkness is someone who gives them warm milk to drink and a piece of bread. Never before has he been so happy with anything as he is with that little jar of warm milk and that morsel of bread. It wakes him up. He sees tall iron things, like fences or warehouse bars, rising all the way to the ceiling of the barrack. After a while he notices that they are beds. All of them are three-tiered, and there are narrow little passageways between them in order to get by. People are in them, lying on straw. Immediately he thinks that he wants to be on top, for those who lie at the bottom or in between cannot even sit up straight in their beds. There are people who are looking at them from their beds because they are new. A woman with a white coat shows mother two beds next to each other, for her and the baby. The two little children will sleep above her.

"I want a top bed," he says, wide awake.

"Can you climb up there?" asks the woman in the white coat. "And won't you fall out?"

"I'm nine years old," he says shortly.

Mother sets the cradle in the bed next to her and lifts the little ones into the middle beds. They lie in the straw, with only their coats off, and sleep. Then she holds him up from behind as he climbs up.

"Don't fall," she says a few times.

When he is on top, rolled up in the straw, mother wants to give him a goodnight kiss, even though it is morning. Mother stands on her toes, and he hangs over the edge, but they cannot reach each other.

"Good night," he says then, unhappily. He sees that mother is trying to laugh but that it is not genuine; she is crying.

He lies on his back and looks at the wooden ceiling right above his head. This is his new house and his new bed. It is quite nice. A strange woman is lying next to him and is sleeping. How odd it is to lie next to a strange woman and not to be able to give a goodnight kiss to your own mother. Oh, well, from now on he will have to kiss her down below, before he climbs up. Then mother will not have to cry.

What day is it today? The day after yesterday. He has in fact passed over a day. Or a night? Then he sleeps.

Housekeeping

THERE IS A school, or a sort of school, at least, with all classes together in one big tent. She is not allowed to attend, however. The school is only for children who will remain here for a while, and she will be going to Poland, thus it is not worth the trouble.

Pooh, it does not matter to her, either. What can you learn in those few days? She came here with father and mother the day before yesterday, and on Monday afternoon the cattle train will be riding into the camp, the train that will take them to Poland on Tuesday. All the children who have been here longer than she have told her this; it is the same thing every week: a long train comes into the camp and stands from Monday afternoon until Tuesday morning, and it must be filled with adults and children before it is time for it to ride away. She and her parents have nothing that would keep them here any longer, thus why would she want to go to school and learn something? They would not even want her there...

And she has enough to do, too. She would have no time to go to school. Father and mother both have to work. Father digs, and mother peels potatoes in the kitchen. Today is their first day, for they just arrived here yesterday, thus they could not yet go to work early in the morning. And now she will be taking care of the beds and the things that have to be put away in the beds. She will also go stand in line when food is being served. When father and mother come back from work for the afternoon meal, perhaps she will already have gotten their food. These are all things that keep her from even *wanting* to go to school.

Yesterday and the day before yesterday she was still able to do everything with mother. It was a good thing, too, for if she had seen all those dirty and dreadful things for the first time without mother...When she came to the washhouse where all the strange women were washing themselves all over, she pulled on her sleeve and said, "Mother—oh, let's go somewhere else!" But mother laughed at her and said, "Silly—there *is* no where else!" And then she understood and she undressed, too, and washed herself under one of the taps, right next to a big, fat woman. She kept her eyes on her tap and on herself, but even though she did not look about her, she *felt* the woman next to her, and that was just as bad.

And later when she was looking for the toilets, mother took her to a little wooden house that was far worse than the washhouse. There were a lot of women there at the same time, and you had to go sit among those strange women. It smelled so nasty there that she became completely nauseated from it. Leaning against mother, she cried and called out, "I *can't* do that! I *can't* do that!" But she *had* to do it. There was a little old woman who found it just as terrible as she did. She sighed and called to God to see this disgrace and punish those responsible for it. But how can you call to God when everything around you is so nasty? Does He hear you then? Can He hear you when there are men talking loudly to each other in the other half of the little house, which is partitioned off from this half by a reed curtain? When it smells *so* nasty and when you are *so* ashamed, then God is far away from you.

No, if mother had not been there with her that first time, she would not have been able to bear it. She herself does not know exactly what "unbearable" is. She thinks about running into the barbed wire—about bleeding—about bleeding to death. But now that more than a day has already gone by, she no longer thinks about such terrible things. She goes to the little wooden house and washes herself in the washhouse, and she does not look and does not think. She makes the beds for the three of them and puts their things away, and she fervently longs for the moment when the steam whistle shrieks over the camp and when father and mother may return to the barrack.

She puts the suitcases and rucksacks on the beds in such a way that they are about at the same level. Then she pulls a cover over them. It has to be neat, just as if it were merely an ordinary bed, not a linen closet and an attic and a kitchen cupboard all at the same time. The blanket must also serve to catch the straw that whirls down from the bed above. Each time that your neighbor above climbs up to her bed to get something, straw rains down below. At night when your neighbor above turns over, it rains straw, too; it makes you sneeze and cough. At night your clothes lie under your mattress; in the morning they are wrinkled and dusty and full of straw. You put your coat on over your pajamas and go to the outside door with your clothes to shake them out. But the outside door serves the men's half of the barrack as well, and it is *so* crowded that you do not know how you are going to move. Then you push yourself back through the narrow little paths between the tall iron bedsteads and, huddled up on your bed, try to get dressed, for there is no room to do it in the narrow passage.

In the washhouse you must wait until a tap is free. You merely splash a little water on yourself, for you want to get away quickly. Mother can do it all much faster; she has already taken the bread and jar of butter out of the suitcase from under the bed and has taken a place at the table in a side corridor between two bedsteads. It is very difficult to get a place. Some people quarrel over it, but mother cannot quarrel—she asks in a friendly manner, and then the people look at her in surprise and make room for her.

But she must wait in line for the coffee that comes from the large pail at the front of the barrack, otherwise father and mother will be late for morning work call. Standing in line is very difficult, for most people push you back. Fortunately the person distributing the coffee sees that she is being pushed back and helps her first. Without spilling them, she brings the three mugs of coffee to the table, and thus father and mother are ready for work call just in time.

Just when she wants to go straighten up her bed, all the people are herded out of the barrack except those who have cleaning duty. There must be no one walking about when the barrack is being cleaned. She wanders a little outside between the barracks and does not know what to do with herself. She does not know anyone here. It is raining, and big puddles have formed; you cannot sit on the wet ground—you would also be stepped upon by all the other people who are walking about. Most of those who are wandering between the barracks in the rain are elderly; people under sixty-five have to work. It is actually more pleasant to be allowed to peel potatoes in the kitchen than not to know where you must go. But they do not have eleven-year-old girls peeling potatoes in the kitchen.

When she is allowed inside again, she hangs her wet coat up on a piece of iron protruding from her bed. The coat is really too wet to lay under the covers. They probably will not say anything about how untidy it looks, hanging up there like that.

She straightens up mother's bed and her own bed and then goes to the men's barrack too make father's bed.

Father sleeps in a bed on the third tier, but that does not matter; she can easily climb up if she steps up on the first and second beds. An old man is sitting on the bottom bed, and he grumbles a little. She does not listen to him, for she cannot help that father sleeps so high, can she? Above, way above, she stretches herself all the way out; you can stand up straight here and look out over all the beds on the third tier.

The third tier is a lot nicer than the second!

Father has left everything lying about in a very untidy fashion. He knew that she would be coming to straighten it up. It is a cozy feeling to know that father is counting on you. She really could not have been going to school, even if they would have wanted her there.

As she lets herself drop down, her skinny legs swinging about in her search for a point of support, she almost kicks the old man. The man grumbles a lot now, but she certainly has not done it on purpose. "Oh, it was an accident," she says, and runs out of the men's barrack.

Should she go stand in line with their three bowls for the midday meal? The food has already been brought inside in large cauldrons, and there is already a long line of people with bowls standing between the beds in the men's barrack. Father and mother have such a short time to eat; it does not matter if their food is a bit cold. She goes to the back of the long line in the narrow passageway and listens to what is being said around her. Two men are joking about standing in line and about the food, which they say they are getting as a gift.

Sighing, a woman behind her complains that she was never used to this. She almost has to laugh about that; grown-ups can say such crazy things! There isn't anyone who was used to this! It is new to everyone, isn't it? The line moves very slowly. When she comes a little closer to the front, she can at least count how many there are before her; in that way it seems much shorter. And when it is finally her turn, she easily says the little sentence that she has repeated to herself again and again: "Three people— father, mother, and I."

"Do you have their cards with you?" asks the man next to the distributor.

"No," she says, "they are at work."

"Then you can't get it now—next."

She cannot help herself and begins to cry. She has stood in line for *such* a long time! But crying will not fill the bowls.

While he puts a deep spoonful of stew into each bowl, the distributor says over his shoulder, "Come later with your father and mother, and I'll let you go in front of the line."

She dries her tears and walks slowly toward the women's barrack. She will find a place at the table and set the bowls down, with the spoons next to them.

But the table is taken, and a fat woman pushes her aside when she comes to the table with her things. "Later! Yes, of course—reserved seats for the young lady!"

She climbs into her bed on the second tier, among the suitcases, and like a sick animal she waits until father and mother return from work.

Dance

THE MEN ARE playing for their lives.

The commandant likes music, and he would like this camp to be a model one. He wants it to include all facets of industry—yes, and art, too.

There are artists enough among the Jews who have

been taken away from their homes and their work. There are masters whose name on a program meant a full house. Well then: they have become the court artists to the commandant. A barrack has been cleared in which the orchestra gives concerts. A uniform has been designed, a dark blue overall with an embroidered lyre on the left sleeve. They rehearse the whole day, just as other inmates of the camp dig or peel potatoes the whole day. There are also a few who are favorite soloists of the commandant. Thus there is a group of Jews who because of their work are temporarily not yet being sent further on: men who are playing for their lives.

When the commandant has house guests in his villa outside the camp, men and women friends with or without a uniform, he can offer concerts to them. Concerts in a full hall, where the audience rises as he enters with his company and does not sit down again before he has sat down; a full house, which does not applaud before he has given the signal. Doesn't he know that warm, living applause breaks forth only when he has left the hall with his company?

A full hall—for to stay away en masse and to thus present an empty hall is forbidden. Even though there has been a transport on that same day, the Jews who have been invited must go out and fill the hall. Even though on that same day the loved ones of the favorite singer have been sent off in a cattle train, the singer must appear on the podium and sing. Oh, and does he sing! He sings "I Pagliacci," with his face that is twisted in rage and repugnance directed toward the commandant. He sings of the children who have been taken from him, of the blood that flows through his veins, just as the blood flows through the veins of the commandant. He sings until his eyes are red and his face is white and grim. The commandant does not understand what is being hurled into his face, and when the song is over he applauds enthusiastically because this enchanting voice has pleased him. There is no deaf man as deaf as this mighty one, no blind man as blind as he—and the commandant does not know it.

It is now Sunday afternoon, thus no one is at work. The winds from the orchestra must present a light program outdoors between the administration barracks. Whoever uses his free afternoon to walk back and forth along the roads of the camp from barbed wire to barbed wire can join the wide ring that is listening to the splashing march music. Whoever is too preoccupied by the thought of Tuesday, which is only one and one-half days away, flees to the barbed wire on the other side of the camp and looks out over the heath that displays the silhouette of the dark forests on the horizon. Whoever cannot bear that, because the heath and forests are free and big and the circle of barbed wire small and limited, walks like a caged animal up and down the paths between the barracks, along the small front yards of the few who are privileged to live in a room instead of in a barrack. He avoids the side by the administration barracks because there the brass instruments are sounding out, clear and happy, into the sunny summer sky.

But the ring around the players is wide and broad, for a day and a half is a long time, and the cattle cars have not yet ridden into the camp to wait for their human cargo. The winds play like carefree children, and the conductor dreams that he is back in the concert halls of the days of long ago. Who is there, then, who is so foolish as to hear in the blaring of the horns and the rolling of the percussion the rattling of wheels that carry off a load of people?

Guards in khaki uniforms with a star on the breast and an SS on the sleeve keep the circle wide. No one is allowed to come too close to the players. Everything is very well regulated here. But a little girl slips through the orderly ring. A little boy follows her, and another and another. The guards see it and let it go. The children are so little, and this offence against the regulations will not be held against those men who are serving with body and soul.

The little boys and girls take each other by the hand and dance to the beat of the cheering music, happy and free and graceful. They dance as if they were not star children but children with a right to freedom, joy, and a future.

Foolish children...

The men are playing for their lives.

Little White Bundle

WE WERE PERMITTED to bring my father to the gate. Two men carried him on a bier covered in white. It is their work, many times per day—their work that keeps them from being sent to Poland.

We walked behind until the gate opened and the two men passed through with their load. My father entered into freedom, but the gate was closed for us.

Oh, he received death in a friendly way; he knew that only death could open the barbed wire and the gate. He nodded to this space, this freedom, in the days of his illness, and now that they are open to him, he has greeted them happily. We lean against the fence, limited and curtailed, and watch him go. What happens to his body is the secret of the little brick house there in the distance. What happens to his soul we will know and understand all the rest of our lives: the good, which is imperishable.

Now I sit leaning against the wall of the hospital barrack, and I try to unravel the network of life and death, of imprisonment and liberation. I try to accept life as kindly as my father accepted death; for now that I have met death in all its generosity, it is difficult for me to turn toward life again.

There are many people walking on the path between

the hospital barracks, even though there are no visiting hours now. People are filing past me, and I do not see them. I see my father's dear face. I see myself standing on the threshold of freedom, and I see a gate that is closed to me. Oh, father, but that is not envy—you know that, don't you? You have always known everything without my having to express it, haven't you?

The only thing from reality I recognize on the path between the hospital barracks is the two men whose work it is to carry a bier. They return, and the bier is empty. The gate has let them in again; they were not permitted to stay outside.

And as the movement on the path becomes hazy again, a greater reality rises within me, slowly liberating me: it is not death that has to open the barbed wire and gate, but the soul itself, grown until it is unassailable, which can rise above the impediments created by harsh hatred and mightiless might. You can live and be free *however* tightly your mortal remains are wedged.

Then I recognize one of the two carriers again. There is no bier, and there is no second assistant. He goes alone, with great steps over the sandy path.

He is carrying something, though. It is too small for a bier. It is too light for the need of an assistant. It is only a little white bundle, absurdly insignificant in the arms of such a big man. It should be in the arms of a mother—but the mother is not there. The man is not being followed by anyone, but the way that he is going is the way to the big gate that will open and then close behind him.

How light it is. How tiny it is. And how great is the freedom that is open to that little white bundle.

Packages

IF YOUR NAME is written on the board that hangs on the wall at the entrance of the barrack, it means that a package has come for you and that father can go to the luggage barrack and pick it up. But his name has never yet been on the board.

Getting a package—perhaps from your friends of the past, without a star—perhaps from the neighbors who have been in your house and have fetched your things for you, things that you could not bring with you—perhaps from that uncle who is married to an aunt without a star and who therefore may remain at home—perhaps...Oh, what nonsense. They know nothing about how you are longing for a package. You may write a postcard only once every two weeks, if your barrack has a writing day; but his barrack has not had a writing day even once, as long as he has been here. How can they know, then, how you are repeatedly going to that board to see if your name is on it—or father's or mother's name, at least? And yet one day their three names are there, underneath one another: father, mother, and he. He does not believe it at first, but when he sees that all three first names are theirs, he gives a shout and goes to mother, panting.

It is after work hours, and mother is sitting on her bed.

"Packages!" he shouts through the passageway, before he has reached her. "For all three of us!"

"Those children with their noise!" grumbles an old woman from a bottom bunk. "They think the barrack belongs to them!"

"Mother, packages for all three of us!" he pants again, when he is standing by mother's bed. Mother suddenly slides down from her bed on the second tier.

"How do you know that?"

"It's on the board. Come with me!"

Yes, she sees it, too, that the first names are theirs.

Father is fetched from the men's barrack, and even before they eat their evening meal, the three of them go to the luggage barrack and do not let themselves be sent back before they are laden with three big packages. There is too much sand blowing about outside to open them there; they must be patient and wait until they are by mother's bed.

The packages are from the neighbors. Mother gives a cry of delight when her very own woolen clothes appear out of her package and all sorts of foodstuffs from her very own stock. The neighbors were thus brave enough to go into their house; they know that those faithful neighbors had risked in doing so, and tears come to her eyes.

"Later," she says, "later we will repay them."

Father smiles sadly into her eyes. "When, later?" he asks. "When we return from Poland?"

But the boy does not hear anything. He pulls the strings off his package with hurried fingers and tears open the paper. Out of the cardboard box comes a large rye bread—good—a jar of butter or something like that—good—a bottle—what is it? Codliver oil! Oh, no...

Disappointment begins to well up in him. Nothing of his own—nothing that is his very own...

Mother, through with her own box, looks tensely with him.

"Codliver oil—it'll get you through the winter, young man! How did they think of it!"

A sweater, yes, that belongs to him—but what is so exciting about clothes?

But then he gives a cheer. His toy engine that you can wind up, whose spring, after a year and a half, is not yet broken! Of course they were not able to pack the whole train, for it would have been too big and too heavy. But the engine is the most important part!

Mother looks sadly at father. Where will the boy be able to play with a locomotive? On the bed? In the sand? And further on, in Poland?

But the boy knows only that it is his possession, his toy, and that the neighbors went into their house to fetch his engine. He gropes further in the box to see if there is anything else. On the bottom lies a pocket atlas of Holland. "Oh!" he calls, delighted. "My atlas! How did they find it!"

He will never know how they found it. He will never know how the neighbors carefully went in, as if it were a burglary, and how in the end they heard a threatening noise, as if they would be raided while at work. He will never know how they groped blindly in his untidy cupboard and had an atlas in hand before they secretly stole away.

What he does know is this: now he can travel wherever he wishes, without the military police seeing him leave the camp from the watchtower—without a furlough—without money.

He can go in bed and lie down on his stomach and travel throughout all of Holland—at least if enough light falls on his bed, the light that shines along all the high bedsteads between him and the little window. Oh, but perhaps there will be no more sandstorm tomorrow, and then he can sit outside beween the barracks or somewhere at the edge of the camp. Then he will have enough light to travel to the smallest village in Zeeland. He can go everywhere, as long as it is far from Drenthe and far from the camp.

And now, now that there is hardly anymore light falling on his bed, he can play with his toy engine. The evening meal? Rye bread with butter, which mother has already prepared for him from what has come out of the packages? He will eat later—or give it here, he can eat it in the meanwhile. There is no space to let the engine ride.

What does that matter? It is his very own toy, and he will let it work however he wants.

He lies on his back in his bed on the second tier. The spring is wound. He turns the engine upside down and lets the wheels turn so fast in the air that you can see only their outline. It sounds like rage, like panting speed, like hoarse hurriedness.

The boy curses from delight.

Hospital Barrack

THE BARRACK DOCTOR has sent her to the hospital barrack because the straw from the bed above her made her cough so much and because she was having tightness in her chest again, just as she had had a few years ago. There are no three-tiered beds in the hospital barrack, only two-tiered ones and a few single ones, without anyone else above them. She lies in a bed on the second tier and thus she is no longer troubled by the straw. Only it is such a shame that in the hospital barrack it smells so dirty from all those hundreds of sick people who cannot go to the washhouse themselves. It might be a while yet before she gets over the coughing and the tightness.

In addition, the windows in the barrack are small, and if by chance there is someone lying under or next to you who cannot bear any draft, then your window is never opened.

And then there are the visiting hours in the evening that you look forward to very much because then father and mother and the children visit you, but then your chest feels much tighter because there are surely a thousand people in the barrack—a thousand people who shuffle and whose talk makes a buzzing noise and who cause a lot of dust to whirl up above. The windows cannot be opened at all, then, because it is dark and the blackout must be in effect.

When the doctor in the hospital barrack comes and asks her how she is, she says each time, "Good, doctor." The doctor cannot change the fact that it smells so nasty and that it is so stuffy and that such terrible things are going on around you.

Underneath her lies a little girl who has a severe abdominal illness. She must be helped the whole day, really, but there are not enough nurses for that. Therefore accidents happen repeatedly, and then the little girl cries because she truly wants to be clean. If the nurse is nice, she says that it is not so bad, but if the nurse is unpleasant, she gives the little girl a scolding, and then she herself would like to cry right along with the child.

On the other side a little further, over there where she can just see from her high bed, lies a woman who is sick in her head. She does not know what she is saying or doing. If she shouts terribly, or if she breaks a lot of things, the nurses give her an injection, and then she quickly falls asleep. Being sick in your head is dreadful—it is much worse than being sick in your belly, or in your ear or anywhere else. People are afraid of you, and you cannot help what you do.

Sometimes people die. Then a screen is placed around the bed, but when you are so high up, the screen does not help. Then she crawls under the covers in order not to see or hear anything; but her chest feels tight under the covers, and she starts to cough, thus she must come out from under the covers again, and the only thing she can do is keep her eyes shut. It is also terrible to see grown-ups cry. When they leave the bed with the screen, they grieve so over the one who has died there. But much worse than crying is when they call aloud, "Now she doesn't have to go on transport—so, at least she doesn't have to go on transport now!" Then it is just as if they are talking to *her*—and she cannot help it, can she?

One day, in the single bed next to her, where from above she *has* to look down, an old woman dies—the whole day long. She would like to flee—but she cannot get out of her bed. The sound would pursue her, too—everywhere. The sound and the face. You cannot look the other way for a whole day, can you? The man and woman who belonged with the old woman were at the bedside for hours, but then they went away to their own barracks. *She* cannot go away; she lies next to the old woman and looks down at her and hears her. Formerly she did not know what dying was. Then she learned about it here and tried to think of it as ordinary. But this—a whole day...

The nurse brings her her midday meal. She *cannot* eat. She really does want to do her best to get better, but

146

how can you eat when you are lying next to an old woman who is taking a whole day to die?

When evening comes, shortly before visiting hours, it is over. But then she has *such* a coughing spell and *such* a choking tightness in her chest that father and mother and the children may come see her for only one moment and are then sent away. She remembers only mother's anxious, frightened face, which throughout the night is continually pushed aside in her memory by the face of the old woman who took a whole day to die.

When father and mother are allowed to come to her again the following evening and when, white and tired, she looks down at them from her top bunk, she no longer has the courage to tell them about yesterday.

What would she tell them? Perhaps they do not even know that it exists: to take a whole day to die. Let them— let them believe that it does not exist...

Transport Night

IT WAS NOT worth the trouble to send her to the children's barrack. Within a week she is going to be sent further on, anyway, and she is fourteen already...

In the children's barrack are all the children who are without a father or mother. They call it the "orphanage," but most of the children do have a father or mother, only they are not here or they are unable to take care of them. Sometimes the parents and the child were hidden separately and the child was taken alone and brought here. Sometimes the parents were in Poland for a long time already and had hidden the child before they went, but now the child has been caught. Sometimes the parents sent the child to Holland from Germany before the war, and now the child no longer knows where his parents are in the world, or *if* they are still in the world. Sometimes the parents were caught before the child was and have already been sent further on. Sometimes the mother is merely in the hospital barrack because she is sick or is having a baby, and there must be someone to take care of the child. Sometimes the children really are orphans for as long as they can remember, and then they know, at least, what has happened to their parents...

But if within a week you are going to be sent further on, and you are fourteen already, then it is not worth the trouble. Father and mother and the other children have already been in Poland for a long time, but they had not found her because the closet in which she had hidden had a door that you could not see. She feels that she would rather not have hidden, for then they would have all gone together. She lived for another couple of months with other people, and now she is going alone.

She is not afraid. She is not afraid of anything. But on Monday afternoon when the train rides into the camp, the long line of cattle cars, dirty and unpainted, and when it remains there along the whole length of the main road— and when she sees the cleaners who are busy scrubbing the inside of the cars and setting down the empty barrels and small casks of water, one to a wagon—and when she sees the paper mattresses being loaded into the few cattle cars that are intended for sick people—then she feels like a little girl, not like a girl of fourteen.

After work hours the people walk back and forth along the main road and look at the cars. When acquaintances meet each other, they look at one another silently and shake their heads. They do not say much. What would they say? Those who have been here longer know it from each Monday afternoon; those who have come here this week are much too shocked to be able to put it into words. Those who know for certain that they must go on the convoy tomorrow are in the barrack packing or are at the administration barrack again to see if there is something to be done.

She does not try. Other people have tried for her, but there is nothing to be done. At least now she will not be shocked when she hears her name called. It is better to know that there is nothing to be done than to still have hope.

The mothers of little children have a lot to pack; she has nothing. She goes to bed early, for she has heard that at three o'clock you are awakened in order to listen to the list being read aloud. She might be able to sleep because she knows for certain that there is nothing to be done. In the midst of the bustle and buzzing and people walking to and fro, she falls asleep right away.

It must be three o'clock, for the woman next to her awakens her and says that she must listen. She does not understand immediately, but she hears the awful silence in the barrack, and then she knows.

Each person must call out "yes" when her name is read: last name, first name, and date of birth. The mothers let their children sleep and call out "yes" in their places.

It will not be her turn for a long time yet because her name comes at the end of the alphabet. But each name gives her a jolt. When the name is of someone she knows, she must control herself so that she does not call out "yes."

There is a mother with five children. Five times she calls "yes," once for herself and four times for the children. Then another name comes; her baby has been forgotten.

"My little one..." she begins, but then she calls wildly, "I'll bring him to the orphanage! I'll not give *one* of my children to them as a gift! Let them forget him, then— they won't get him!"

"Quiet, please!" says the man who is reading the list.

"Presently I'll bring him to the orphanage, before we go into the cattle train!"

"And later, when he is sent further on alone, then?"

says a quiet old woman, who herself has already had to call "yes."

The mother is still. She bends low over the sleeping baby, then straightens up and screams, "You've forgotten my little one!"

"Later!" calls the man, "Now first quiet, please!"

The list continues. "Yes" is called again and again.

Then comes a name that receives no answer. The name after it, which is the same last name with a different first name and birth date, receives no answer, either.

"Answer, please!" calls the man, and he repeats the two names. She knows them; they are two sisters with sweet, elderly faces, who are together the whole day. But they do not answer.

"Who is near them?" asks the man impatiently.

"I am!" calls a woman's voice.

"Look, then, to see why they don't answer."

There is a long period of silence. Then the woman's voice calls, "Be-cause-they-are-dead! Do you understand me?"

"You must speak more clearly!"

"Be-cause-they-are-dead! Do you understand me?"

At first there is silence. Then the women speak in dim, suppressed tones.

"They were right to do it. When you don't have any-one else..."

"Would you have done it, too?"

"I...no...I wouldn't dare."

"Too bad that they didn't wait until the train left. Now two others will have to go in their places."

"Nebbish—how can you say that?"

"It's so, isn't it?"

"Silence!" calls the man. He has looked to see if it were true, and he has seen that it is. He must continue reading the list now.

The girl lies quiet and paralyzed in her bed. Her name has not been called yet, but she is no longer think-ing of her name. She is thinking of the two elderly sisters who do not have to go on the convoy now. Would she

150

herself have wanted to do something like that, if she had known how to do it? No—she would rather live, and try to see if there were a small chance to go on with her life later on, and to have it good. No, oh, no—something good can still happen!

When her name is called, she says "yes" in a small voice that is heard nevertheless. Each voice is heard because each voice sounds out loudly in contrast with the silence of the dead women.

The Z is past.

"Thank you," says the man. He must quickly go ask what is going to happen further with the two dead sisters in this barrack and who will go in their places.

A silence remains hanging before the women begin to pack.

Then comes the voice of a mother who is right near the girl—a mother of three children.

"Come, boys, get dressed! God is just as well in Poland as here!"

The girl sits straight up in her bed, and in doing so she bumps her head against the iron bands of the bed above her.

Is it true what that mother over there says? She has not thought about it at all. She thought that God was not here in this dark barrack, with all that sorrow, with two dead sisters; she thought that God could not be in the cattle cars—and that further on He could not be there at all. But when this mother says it, in such a happy voice...

She lets herself slide out of her second-tiered bed. Her bare feet touch the floor that is full of sand and straw and papers. She clutches the arm of this mother.

"May I go with you?" she asks in a small voice. "I'm alone."

"Of course, dear," says the woman. "If we get into the same car, at least."

"Can you arrange it so that we get into the same car?" she implores. "I thought...I think...that God is closer to you."

The woman kisses her.

"He is in all the cars," she says. "But you stay with me."

The child begins to dress and to pack. She is strangely comforted.

No—she would not want to do what those two elderly sisters did. Ever.

Nursery

LITTLE CHILDREN ARE there, and babies are there—but first and foremost are the flies.

Now that the high bedsteads have been removed, in between which some cribs and cradles stood, and now that there are only little wooden beds painted green, each person who puts his head around the corner of the door says, surprised and mollified, "Oh, how sweet!" And when that head withdraws, just in time not to see any further, that person takes with himself the comforting thought that there is a small oasis to be found in the star desert: no beds above one another, no iron, no darkness, but a light-green color and white sheets, a floor that is scrubbed, and the beds neatly in a row.

Well—in reality it is not light-green and white; in reality it is black—black from the flies.

Who is going to get rid of the flies that find their way from the dung heap right by the camp and the children's barrack, to the dirty, unwiped little noses, the sweating hands, the wet diapers, the running ears of the little children and the babies? It is the job of the flies to point out what is infected and dirty. They live by this work and are comfortable in doing so.

The little noses and ears are infected because the sand from the star desert comes blowing fiercely inside through the holes in the screen that protects the open space of the door when it is too warm to keep the door closed. The sand comes blowing through the sloping trap windows that now and then must be opened to make the hothouse livable. The sharp, blowing sand penetrates the eyes and noses and ears and makes the children sick. Then come the flies that the powerless little fists cannot drive away, and those flies bring their filthy spoils over to the new, healthy children. And so it happens. You do not live with impunity in a desert, not when you are small and defenseless and have been snatched away from a safe home.

He who is concerned about the nursery and who feels power in himself to fight against sickness and suffering, against the children's complaint of homesickness, and the attention from their eyes—he who feels this power is suddenly paralyzed when a sleeping little face is hidden under a black, moving curtain of flies. He knows then that the enemy carries the children off roughly and without pity, but that the flies, small and buzzing and disgusting, will devour them. He knows, too, that you cannot fight against both the coarse dirtiness of powerful men and the small dirtiness of devouring flies.

And yet, he who is concerned about the nursery knows that the good moments are short and costly and that suddenly, on a Monday night and Tuesday morning, they can be broken off. In fierce defense against the enemy he hurries to create more good moments for these who-knows-how-short little lives. He knows that weapons and hate will not achieve what the unceasing will to do good achieves—flashes of happiness, taken by the children and held until death pulls that happiness out of their hands.

The big girls who take care of the children are themselves still cared for in the children's barrack. Among the big girls are some who have lost the meaning of the word "home" long ago. They have been fugitives almost as long as they can remember. They were perhaps taken in by a family, but they were guests—guests, who could still write to their own parents—until even that stopped. They no longer know if they still have parents. Then they were taken away from the family that lodged them and brought here.

This is what life means to these young caretakers: fighting for your good right to live—fighting to be the first and to get the most—seeing to it that you are not pushed back—seeing what can be taken back from all that has been taken away from you in life.

These children must give love to powerless little ones.

Love? Where do you get that? What does that look like? What can you achieve with it? What can you get for it in exchange? Such chatter! When it comes to the really important things in life, love won't get you anywhere!

You do your work because you will be sent on convoy if you have no work and are not useful. You do it well and above all, quickly, because perhaps you will attract attention as a good hand and then can profit by it. You do your work perfunctorily because you cannot do it quickly otherwise, and "haste" is the word that adults and children drag along in this desert. You do it until the minute in which you have the right to retreat. You are tired and agitated, and you want to climb up on your bed in the girls' dormitory and play with the few things that you possess.

Oh, yes, there are some nice little children in the group. Pretty little faces, cute in their movement—sweet to be seen with them. You pick one out for your favorite, and in your free time, or also in the time when you actually should be cleaning the room or should be busy with a whole group, you dawdle around with your favorite and act nice with it. You know that you look good when you have such a pretty child in your arms—just like a very young mother. The other girls joke about it and call to you, "Your child is crying!" You also see to it that your favorite receives extras, sweets or food or a very pretty dress. You are *so* accustomed to taking care that you yourself receive as much as possible that you do it for this little child, too, because it has become a part of yourself. In this manner you can endure life, at least; you would not be able to if you were busy the whole day with all those dirty noses and with those children who are of no use to you and who are not at all attractive.

Sometimes there is inspection by a service leader or someone or other who has more say in the camp than the people in the children's barrack. Then everything is turned topsy-turvy. Before inspection—and that is always very early, thus you must rouse the children from their sleep, even though inspection usually takes place later than the appointed hour, or not at all—all the beds are moved from their places, and then everything is washed and mopped and the beds are tightly made. The children are not allowed to play or to spill anything while eating, otherwise all the trouble would be for nothing. You would like to shake them sometimes, when just before inspection is to occur, they dirty a bed that has just been cleaned. And when inspection finally takes place, you quietly draw yourself toward the bed of your pet and take him in your arms and are affectionate with him. You can always calculate that the inspector is looking at you; he will say nice things to you, then, and remember that you are so good with children. That can never hurt.

This work *is* bearable. And you have old rights in this camp because you have been here longer than the other children, thus you might not be sent further on. It all comes to this: to get more than another, to attract more attention than another, and not to be sent further on.

The little children do not know that. They are defenseless against power, injustice, treachery, and the privileging of a few. Their defenselessness has brought them here. Their only defense is the complaint in their eyes. But the flies do not see that complaint, and the driving sand and the diseases that are prevalent do not see the complaint, and these big girls, whose deformed souls are themselves a denunciation against the world into which they were born, these big girls do not see the complaint, either. That is why the children's defenselessness is so complete.

Oh, but they will be avenged! Whether they live or not—they will be avenged! They will not let the cry from their toothless mouths be silent, they will not let the complaint in their wide-open eyes be dimmed until the end of days! There will be *no* rest for those who have perpetrated this—*no* peace for those who have dragged these infants out of their cherished homes and have thrown them together in one deathly heap—*no* rest, *no* peace, as long as the echo of the cries of those little children shall be heard, as long as the reflection of that complaint in their eyes shall be seen. They are mighty, these defenseless ones. Their might reaches to the end of the world—to eternity.

Tucking In

THERE IS MAGIC in the tucking in of children. He who is an observer would be able to look at the magician's hands to know when the moment of the miracle is there; and he would suddenly notice that it is over and that the moment has escaped him. But the magician himself cannot seize that moment, either. He knows that his hands have made the quiet motion of folding blankets around a child's little body and that it happened then without his knowing it: a beaming smile on a satisfied little face—a thumb in the mouth—and eyes slowly veiled under falling lashes.

She who has gone about the nursery and has tucked everyone in, child by child, gently closes behind herself the door to the magic room, where sleep has crept in on feather-light feet. In the corridor she examines her hands to see whether they can betray the secret of the miracle. What is it with those hands? They are a mother's hands. Oh, come now—there is no miracle in them! The world is full of mothers' hands, isn't it? And is the world full of miracles? Perhaps...

He is a tall boy who is three years old, and actually he is too big for a crib. But because he is helpless and dirty like a baby and does not say anything and cannot make anything clear, his bed must be placed among those of the babies.

The big girls have no patience with him. Goodness, such a big lout! If he were a baby—well, that is part of your work. But this—let others clean him up.

The flies *do* pay attention to his crib. They feel minutely whether someone will defend himself or whether he has given up the struggle. *He* has given up the struggle. He lies dead-still as his little face, his hands, his legs are covered with flies. Only a soft wail indicates that they are bothering him.

But his mother, who is in the hospital, says that he was a happy child who talked and laughed and played and walked just like any other three-year-old. When he was taken from his bed in the night, because the men in green had come to fetch them, he said his last sentence: "I don't want to!" Then he was silent. He is still silent.

"I don't want to! I don't want to belong to your world, you big cowards, who threaten little children and take their good world away from them! I don't want to become a grown-up like you! I want to be a baby in a cradle, and I'll remain one, too! Do what you want—take little children out of their beds and their homes and take away their toys—*I* don't belong in your world! I don't want it! Do you understand me? Do you understand me?"

The flies do not understand him. But the one who tucks him in understands him; her eyes penetrate his fixed gaze and take his wordless secret away from him. She presses the covers securely around the listless little body.

"Sleep well, fellow!"

He smiles like a little boy who is three. No—like an old man who has grown wise throughout life, and tired.

Most likely she is the youngest of all of the children in this group who has served time in prison. Are there many released convicts who are not yet two years old? Oh, yes; there are some who were not yet born and shared a cell with their mothers and other women. Those children are even younger than two.

Her crime? For naturally crime precedes imprisonment—a crime committed by the one who is imprisoning, or a crime committed by the one who is in prison. No one is imprisoned unless a crime has been committed.

Well—she pretended that she was not a star child. She was cared for in a house that was not a star house. Then they tracked her down and put her in prison. That is all.

Did she have it good there? She cannot tell you about it, for her broken little sentences are more like cheers than words. She cheers about life and because everyone is nice to her. She does not know that her happiness is reflected in the faces across from her and that therefore everyone seems nice. She did not lose that happiness in prison, thus perhaps she had it good.

Do her father and mother know that she is no longer in the house that was not a star house? Do they know that she was in prison? Do they know that she is here and that she makes the whole nursery happy with her happiness, happiness that they, the parents, actually were entitled to have? Are they still there? Have they been found, too, and have they already traveled further on? Are they still living?

Oh, come—who asks such foolish questions now! Presently, when she is sent further on, what does it matter if a father and mother remain behind or are in Poland, living or dead? It does not make any difference, does it? Isn't everyone nice to her?

She curls herself comfortably into the position to be

tucked in: a little animal on four legs, the head pressed stiffly into the pillow.

"Sleep well!"

Through a crack in her closed eyelids a world of joy looks up.

There is a little girl who cannot laugh because she has been sent here from another camp, a camp where children are broken of laughing. With frightened eyes she follows the tucking-in ceremony in the other beds; if she should be forgotten!

She does not want to eat, and she does not want to talk, and she cannot laugh. But she does want to be tucked in. It is her good right, after that previous camp, to receive something good without giving anything up in exchange. A smile? She cannot. A word, even a broken one? She does not want to. Only her eyes speak. Threatening, they say, "Don't pass me over! Don't you dare pass me over! If I should reconsider about eating a little porridge tomorrow— remember: if you have in mind to pass me over, I'll *never* eat again!"

But who would even think about passing her over? Even if all attempts to teach her to laugh fail, she will be tucked in.

No, even more that that; something happens to her tonight that does not happen to any of the other little children. Wrapped in a blanket, she is taken out of her bed and carried to the corridor. Not for the doctor, not to have an eardrum lanced—no, no, nothing like that—only to learn to laugh.

In a corner of the corridor, there where the legs of boys running past cannot reach, sits a young kitten, just as crouched and just as suspicious as she is herself. The kitten is taken from its hiding place and petted. Petting and tucking in are almost the same. The green eyes of the crouched, suspicious kitten also say, "Watch out if you pass me over!"

Seriously and attentively she sees how the kitten lets

itself be petted. She sees the big eyes close slowly, and she hears a satisfied humming sound. Even if she cannot laugh, she can see and hear very well.

Then her hand is led to the kitten's velvety back. She pets it. The little girl who is afraid of being passed over when all the children are tucked in—the little girl pets the kitten. Petting and tucking in are the same thing.

The kitten is sleepy. Suddenly it begins to yawn; it displays a wide, pink mouth and a pointed, curled little tongue.

And then she laughs. A hoarse, unpracticed little sound—eyes that are wrinkled in the corners—a mouth that becomes broad in the white little face—cheeks, and a nose that turns up.

She can return to the nursery and to her bed now. She is tucked in, of course. Who would dare to pass her over?

"Sleep well!"

The smile remains even as she sleeps.

He is four years old and one of the biggest children here. But even if you are big, you still want to be tucked in; even if you are six—even if you are eight—oh, you want to be tucked in when you are even much older than that.

Each evening he looks at the hands that tuck him in. He looks up, along the arms, at the face. He wants to have something that will not be taken away from him, just as his home and his father and mother were taken from him, and later just as his new home where he had been hidden and then found, was taken away.

Each evening he asks the same thing.

"Will you *always* be my aunt?"

And each evening he receives the same answer and each evening he is satisfied.

"Yes—always."

Always. That means: "yes—until one night when you are dressed and one morning when you are put in a cattle car and taken somewhere where I cannot follow you. I'll be your aunt until then."

And each evening he smiles happily at the word "always."

"Sleep well, my boy!"

How long will "always" last?

But you are not finished with this new little child by just tucking her in. You can be tucked in if there is a bit of rest in you, or at least the desire for rest. How can you rest when your little face is wet with tears and your little body is racked with sobs!

She is calling for her big sister. But her big sister cannot be with her all the time; she must remain a girl among other girls, not a worn-out little mother.

Mother is not there anymore. Almost a year ago when that other baby was born, the baby that did not want to live and immediately went away again, then mother quietly went with him. That happens more often, mothers going away with children who do not want to live, but this mother really could not be missed. And now when the big sister cannot be with her all the time, such as now—how, then, can she keep from sobbing and let herself be tucked in?

Tucking in no longer helps in this case; this little girl needs a lap.

But in the lap she keeps sobbing and calling for her big sister. She *cannot* give herself over to the warmth of the lap, she *cannot* settle herself in the arms that envelop her. Only the voice becomes weaker, and the little head nods to the side.

Until suddenly sleep closes her eyes. With difficulty she raises her heavy eyelids up again. Resigned, she lays her head against that cherishing softness which she had at first pushed away and, half-sleeping, mumbles a long-forgotten word: "Mama."

She is carried to her bed and tucked in.

"Sleep well."

She does not hear it.

But the little girl who has no name because they found her without a card or without something that could identify her—she cannot be tucked in here tonight. She must go to the hospital, and quickly, for although sick children belong in the nursery, dying children do not.

Come, little girl without a name—smile at me before you go away! Can't you do that, with those shadows on your little face? Look at me—come on! Can't you do that, with those eyes that no longer have a hold on anything? Do you no longer know that not even a week ago you rocked your head to the music when I sang another baby to sleep? Do you no longer know of all the evenings when I tucked you in—only yesterday?

Now I know that you can die of a broken heart, even if you are just one year old. You innocently catch a childhood illness, and you lay yourself down and no longer want to live. Then death comes with gentle hands and lays shadows on your face and tucks you in.

"Sleep well, little girl without a name!"

Presently, when you awaken on the other side, say, then, that you have no name and show them your broken heart. Then they will give you a name, for all time, and a new, happy heart. The broken heart will be saved; that will remain—remain—together with all the other broken little hearts—until the end of days.

Bogeyman

THEY ARE COMING back from visiting their mothers in the hospital. For three quarters of an hour they were permitted to be there and to scratch around at the foot-end of a bed, or to sit *very* still and not fall out, if the bed was a top one. They have been stuffed full of treats from the packages that the mothers have received or with milk that the mothers secretly have saved from what they were supposed to drink in order to get better. The little ones might be wet tonight from all the vicissitudes and good things to eat—but what does it matter? Après nous le déluge!

There is still the glorious return trip to make: to walk at the hand of a grown-up on legs that are not very fast, among the houselike barracks that have windows with real curtains and front gardens with real flowers. That is a world that they get to see only when they go visit their mothers in the hospital. That is *the* world. The world is strangely beautiful.

In one of the small front gardens are marigolds, rich and abundant. Marigolds, growing and blooming in the desert. But the flowers are only in the gardens of those who live in a room that looks like a room of a house—it is true that two or three families live there together, but still they live in a room and not in a barrack, and therefore they have a feeling of being established, of not having to continue wandering—for the time being...The flowers belong to those who have put down roots in the desert ground and who will be more hurt than the others in the barracks, for presently their roots will be pulled up, too. Presently...And the flowers, which are more deeply rooted than the people, will remain.

The bright-orange color of the marigolds draws the little children. One child breaks loose from the grown-up's hand and wants to take the flowers, pull them up, have them.

"No, you can't do that. Those flowers belong to other people."

A difficult concept, when you are always in a dormitory, in a mass, and when you have to share all the toys, and have nothing that belongs just to you yourself except a mother, but she is in the hospital.

The little one at the grown-up's other hand understands more about it—at least he *wants* to understand more—at least he wants to *pretend* that he understands more. He nods respectably, with his mouth tightly shut and his eyes threatening.

163

"No, right? You must not do that. You must not take what belongs to other people, right? Otherwise you'll go on transport!"

Hora

THERE ARE BIG children in the children's barrack as well as little ones; there are boys and girls with a job, a job outside the barrack. They work in one of the camp industries, they even learn a trade or work as an orderly to one of the powerful Jews in the camp. An orderly is the most important profession. You feel powerful yourself, for you can keep people waiting until they are admitted, you can pantingly deliver a hurried message and say that there is not a moment to lose. Having power is something very pleasurable; you see nothing else before you in this camp: of the men in green exerting power over Jews—of Jews over Jews—of caretakers over children—of children over children. It is a pleasant feeling to belong to the group that has the power rather than to the group in submission. You forget, then, that you are a prisoner in a camp and are behind barbed wire. And when you have command over adults, then everything is quite all right.

Those who are learning a trade do not belong to the group who hold power. They must listen to the overseer or assistant overseer, or to other students who have been there longer. But you *learn* a trade, and you gain something from it. Later, when everything is back to normal in the world, and you know a trade...

The younger children go to school in the children's barrack. The room, which is in the middle of the barrack between the dormitories, is a mess hall and school and shul and everything else at the same time. Sometimes there is a young couple in the camp that wants to get married in a Jewish ceremony so that they can be sent further on together, and then the mess hall in the children's barrack immediately becomes a wedding hall. That room actually serves as everything for the whole camp. There is a folding door in the back by the sand desert, and if the dust is not blowing or if it is not raining, the door can be left open. Then it is a real room, and the desert seems like a real garden. If the room is not a school but a shul, then the cabinet is used for holding the rolls of the Torah. If the room is not a shul but a school, then the one board is used for all the classes; it has no stand, and there are no nails in the wall for it, and therefore it is placed on a chair or a bench or whatever. When the room is not a school but a mess hall, then the tables stand in long rows, and enamel or tin plates and bowls are set down on the rough wood. The children have it much better here than in the big barracks, for they can sit and do not have to stand in a long line to get their food.

Sometimes there are many men and women teachers, four or five. The children can then be divided up into classes just like in a real school—except the groups at the tables all sit right on top of each other and are confused by what the teacher or the children in the other classes are saying and doing and are confused by all the men and women and children in or outside the barrack who are walking through the room the whole day long. Yet there are wonderful moments, especially when a story is told to the whole school or when all the children sing together.

But sometimes there are very few teachers all of a sudden—after Tuesday. You never see those teachers again, and thus the school must be divided up very differently or else taken all together in one group. Oh, well, but then there are usually many fewer children, too, after such a Tuesday...

There were a couple of times when the school was permitted to walk outside the camp. They were counted at the gate by a military police officer, and when they returned there was a guard in uniform who was with them in order to see to it that no child or teacher ran away. It was *so* wonderful to see the heath and the forest. Star children from the city had not been permitted to see that for such a long time—an ordinary farm with real people without uniforms and without stars and with haystacks and cows and pigs and goats and sheep. It was *so* wonderful that you had to scream and shout from pleasure and freedom, so wonderful that you had a strange pain later, when you thought about it. But now that is over for good, for one time in the other school there was a teacher who ran away and was never found, thus the commandant has now said that no one may go out of the camp anymore except the few who work outside the camp, where they are watched *so* closely that they cannot get away alive.

Oh, the school children have fun sometimes, except on Tuesday—but that does not count.

Now there is just one man teacher and one woman teacher remaining after the past Tuesday. They take the whole school together because there are not many children remaining, either, and because you cannot really work with the big and little children all mixed together. The teachers tell stories and they sing, and sometimes a child has something to tell and they have a good time together, the remaining children and the remaining adults. Later, when again a new convoy from the cities comes to the camp, there will perhaps be teachers in it or sometimes a whole lot of children, and then the school will change again.

The folding door is open. The sun is shining on the sand, and the wind and dust are not blowing. How could you ever want your own house and your own city back again? Besides, there are two more days before it is Tuesday. Two days are a lot, when the sun is shining and the doors are open.

A little boy of five years is playing in the sand by the barbed wire. And then, without respect for the school, he comes walking toward the open door. He is singing a Hebrew song that he has learned from the big children, and it is a song that he does not understand. He is singing with his mouth wide open and his head leaning backwards from heartfelt enjoyment of the sun, without thinking about the school that he is entering and where they have been sitting quietly and listening to him.

He is singing as unconsciously as only a child can sing in a language that he does not understand:

> Ashreinu! Ashreinu!
> Ma tov, ma tov ḥelkenu!
> Ma yafa, ma yafa yirushateinu
> Ashreinu!

Some of the big children understand it. The teachers understand it, too, and the child singing so unconsciously keeps them under a spell of happiness.

> How lucky are we! How lucky are we!
> How good, how good is our share!
> How beautiful, how beautiful is our lot!
> How lucky are we!

Then one of the adults takes the child by the arm and walks with him outside in the sun. Without a word, the whole school follows her. Outside they sing, they sing, and the whole time it is the same song: that they are so lucky and that their lot is so good. They do not know it, but suddenly they notice that they are standing in a wide ring with their hands set upon each other's shoulders. They dance the hora, the round dance of free children of Palestine. Those who cannot dance the hora stand in a circle around them and clap their hands to the beat of the song: that they are so lucky and that their lot is so good.

In the midst of the barbed wire. In the sun.

> Ashreinu! Ashreinu!
> Ma tov, ma tov ḥelkeinu!

For between now and Tuesday are two more long, sunny days.

See Again

IT IS LATE in the evening, and only the big children are still sitting in the mess hall. Suddenly there is a group standing there, a group of children, sleepy and pale and blinking in the light; they were captured together in a house where aunts without stars had hidden them. The aunts are in prison, say the biggest children, who are the most awake. It was not permitted, was it, to hide star children and take care of them and be good to them; you go to prison for doing that, if it is noticed.

You ask what their names are? Well, which name, the former one or the one given in the aunts' house? The former one, for now they have it back again. The big children still know their former name, and they say it with the fervent pleasure of an old recollection. The smaller ones have forgotten their former name. They cannot think of it—really they cannot—not even after they are refreshed by sleep.

A few of the big children see Hebrew letters written on the school board. Goodness, they still know them! Oh, you want to hear the letters? Of course they still know them! It has been a long time since they have seen them, hasn't it?

They eat and drink, except those children who cannot stay awake, and then in the over-filled dormitories, beds are made empty in order to lodge the newcomers. They have become a part of the children's barrack now.

It is strange to be called by your former name. If you

are a boy, it is strange to have a little cap on your head during prayers that are said before and after meals. You fold your hands during the prayers, just as you learned to do in the aunts' house, and when you see that none of the others is doing that, you play around a bit with your fingers and do not know what to do with them.

"Later you'll get another Savior, won't you?" Dreamy and confused you then ask this question to another boy who looks as though he will not laugh at you.

"You? You're Jewish, too, aren't you?"

"Oh, yes—that's true," you say, resigned. It is difficult to make out, for the aunts were nice and meant it seriously when they spoke of the Lord Jesus and when they said that you must never forget your prayers. They say a prayer here, too, but a very different one...

That is better, too, for you are going to be sent to Poland because you are a Jew, and you will be going together with all Jewish children. Thus you really do have to be one of them. You must rid yourself of that confusion that has come into you, from the time you noticed that the aunts took the Lord Jesus seriously and that here they take the one and only God just as seriously. Grown-ups take everything seriously, and they want you to believe them. You want very much to do that, but which of the two? The Jews?

Yes, the Jews; because you are going to be sent to Poland with the Jews.

But the aunts are in prison...

The one boy who has come here along with the other new children but who was not living with the aunts dressed himself very hurriedly on the morning after his arrival and asked whether you may walk outside here. Behind the barrack is a stretch of sand that is blocked by barbed wire, and there the children may walk as much as they want. He then ran outside, and there he walked back and forth, the whole time back and forth, with short steps, with long steps, and with his arms waving forcefully. The whole time he walked back and forth. After breakfast he continued it. When school began he said that he would like very much to go to school, but just this once could he walk back and forth for a while longer? Well—he could. Finally he was *so* tired and was panting *so* much that he had to go sit down and get a mug of milk. When he was rested, he knocked softly on the door of the schoolroom and asked if he could still come in.

"I kicked up quite a racket, didn't I?" he said to the boy next to him during a break.

"Why did you do such a crazy thing?" asked his neighbor good-naturedly.

"I was in a room for a whole year," he said dryly. "For a whole year I didn't go outside, so that they wouldn't catch me. You become dull from that, let me tell you! And now they've caught me anyway. But I don't mind."

"Not even if they send you further on?"

"Well, no. I'd be outside, wouldn't I?"

After a while his neighbor asked, "Were they nice to you there?"

"At first they were. But later my father and mother were caught for sure, in the place where they had gone into hiding, for then the money didn't come anymore. And without money they couldn't buy food, they said. Oh, I was so hungry! We sure get a lot to eat here!"

"Oh, yes?" said his neighbor, flattered. He feels responsible for the reception of the new guests, for he has been here a long time.

That afternoon, at the midday meal, the neighbor took care to sit next to him again. He traded his plate for that of the new boy's because his own had more food on it.

After a few days of deep thinking the little girl with the dark curls knows her former name. It comes out dreamily, as if pronouncing the name causes a lost world to arise.

The grown-ups then go searching and working because that name appears in the camp's lists of names. There are penal barracks where grown-ups go if they had hidden and then were found. They must work very long hours and wear strange blue overalls with red shoulders.

The men are shaved bald, but fortunately the women are not. A woman is found in these barracks whom they think is the mother of the little girl. That woman is permitted between work hours to come to the children's barrack under supervision of a guard. She is warned that perhaps she will see her little girl again.

When she sees her little girl again—and it is her little girl—and she has her in her arms after a long, long year, then she loses all control. Her cries and her daughter's cries fill the room and seem to reverberate against the walls. All the others are silent, afraid and ashamed.

"How beautiful you are! How beautiful you are!"

Is it crying? Is it laughing? Now and then she holds the child at arm's length in order to look at her and then pulls her back toward herself.

"How beautiful you are!"

Then, quiet at last, she takes a comb out of the pocket of her overalls and combs the child's curls with long, curved, caressing strokes.

Celebrations

DOES THE COMMANDANT know that these Jews not only carry their Judaism in their hearts throughout the world but that, either openly or in secret, they live it in this camp as they never did in times of freedom? Even if the commandant already knows it, then he still has no suspicion of how unassailable it makes them. He is letting his enemy keep the strongest weapons and is taking only the unimportant things away: a bit of freedom, a few possessions, some outward dignity, a bit of health, and—well, a bit of life.

The atmosphere in the children's barrack is busy and industrious; a sukkah is being built. A sukkah is being built farther up in the camp, too, by children who live in the big barracks with their fathers and mothers. But the sukkah of the children's barrack must be the prettiest.

Only one wall is needed; the other three are formed by the bay in the barrack's outside wall. The roof consists of bunches of straw, which could easily be saved from the supply of straw that is intended for the mattresses for the whole camp. Through the straw you see the sky, and it has to be that way, too, for otherwise it is not a sukkah; otherwise this hut is not a reminder of how the forefathers of these children left slavery in Egypt behind them and gave themselves over to the protection of God Who would lead them through the barrenness in the desert.

The sukkah is even more open, even more unprotected than the barracks—and yet mealtimes in this narrow sukkah are a feast.

The preparation, the work accomplished by big hands and little ones, is even more beautiful than the celebration itself. The children's barrack is glittering in gold and silver. Strips, snips, and sheets have found their way to the children's barrack from the paper foil industry in the camp, an industry that creates a quiet, sedentary type of slave labor for the elderly who cannot do any heavy work. The sukkah must be beautiful, decorated in their own taste, with their own touch. Didn't their forefathers live in their portable homes for forty years, and didn't the tents at that time have the personal household goods of those who dwelled in them? But their homes remained portable; the forefathers went from the one camp to the other. Perhaps the train that rides into the camp on Monday is an even more obvious reminder of the wandering through the desert than this decorated sukkah is. But you cannot see the sky through the roof of the cattle train...

Winter has come, and the holiday of Hanukkah is near. The menorah in the mess hall is made ready with lights to celebrate the miracle of the deliverance from an oppression like this one. It now seems that the commandant is beginning to understand how weak lights can radiate power. You defend yourself against intangible power with a ban; against tangible power you defend yourself with barbed wire and bullets and whatever makes life flow out of mortal bodies. A ban can be transgressed when the intangible power makes the fear for the preservation of this bit of mortal life vanish. Does the commandant know how much more difficult it is to fight against intangible power than against the tangible?

On the first night of Hanukkah the ban comes: no celebrating of any holiday, in any form, either Jewish or Christian. This menorah is already burning when it is evident that the ban is not a rumor but an official order that has been spread around the camp. This first evening has already been a festival of lights—that cannot be undone. But tomorrow evening, when the menorah is supposed to hold two candles—and this whole week, when the number of lights is increased until there are eight in a row...

The little children cannot think about anything beyond today. The bigger children go to bed with sulking thoughts about the celebration that was taken away from them.

And then it happens—a small technical thing that can happen anywhere and on any day. On the second day there is a power failure in the whole camp and far beyond it—even in the villa of the commandant.

Everything is in the dark. But that cannot be, where adults and children walk in confusion through the big barracks by the hundreds, where masses of children are stacked up in the high beds of the dormitories. A light must be kept on.

Then two warm, wavering lights shine, more clearly than when they were overpowered by the electric light. The little lights shine through the darkness of the full room and lay a festive gleam on sound young faces. For it is the second evening of Hanukkah.

How difficult it is to defend yourself against intangible power, which radiates from a bit of candlelight...

Pied Piper of Hamelin

ONE OF THE children in the girls' dormitory has a father with a violin. He may remain here still because he plays in the orchestra. But they say that the commandant will not be permitted to keep the orchestra much longer; his superiors do not want an orchestra in the camp. And when the orchestra no longer exists, then that father and that child might be sent further on. But it has not yet come to that, and as long as it has not, then each day should be as pleasant as possible. That father with the violin has said so, and in order to make the day as pleasant as possible he comes with his violin to the girls' dormitory one evening, before the younger girls have gone to sleep.

The little ones in the first tier of beds are already tucked in. The bigger girls on the second tier are playing and talking on their beds. The very big girls who sleep on the third tier are not all present, but some have taken out their possessions and have displayed them on their beds. When the tall man with the happy face comes into the room with his violin case, the little ones crawl out from under the covers, and those on the second and third tiers lean over the edge to see what is going to happen.

He does not say anything. He winks at his daughter, who winks back. Both of them still know what it was like at home. They both still know of how often the father played at her bedside when it was time to go to sleep. This seems like home; it is a bit different, but you cannot think about that if you want each day to be as pleasant as possible.

He takes out his violin, tunes it, and puts it under his chin. Each movement is followed by all those children on the first, second, and third tiers. There are even a few little girls who have, without knowing it, carefully grasped an imaginary violin in their hands and have put it under their chins. Their eyes and hands are full of reverence.

"What will it be?" asks the man.

The voices from the beds call out children's songs, school songs, and Hebrew songs all mixed together. He catches upon one and plays. Leaning over the bars of the foot-end of all the beds are children's heads, watching. Only those who are lying very close to him remain blissfully under the covers, their faces turned toward him. No one is singing anymore; singing you can do any day, but a violin you hardly ever hear. A violin that plays songs, one after another—songs that you still know from the past...

He no longer asks what he should play. He chooses the songs himself. Or does the violin choose for him? Just for a while let the violin be the master over him when he is not playing music for his life. Presently he might have to leave the violin behind, and then others will be the masters over him, and the violin will remain alone, without anyone drawing songs from it. Oh, well, he will take it one day at a time.

He is no longer playing the children's songs. A quiet, comforting tune is penetrating into the farthest corners of the room. The big girls are hanging far over the edge of their beds. Those on the second tier are lost in thought and listen with their calm faces supported in both hands. But the little ones have quietly crawled back to the little hollow under their covers and with wide eyes look into the emptiness there.

Where are they, anyway? Not in a star desert and not in a dormitory with high iron bedsteads. Each one has glided back toward her own world, a world that none of the others knows about. No one can follow them, and no one may follow them; this is their own journey to their own home. Quiet...let them go. They have wings that fly above barbed wire, above watchtowers, over a wide heath, and then each girl goes her own way. Quiet...no one will betray what is reflected in their dreaming eyes.

Has it become a lullaby? Just what does the violin want to do? Is that a man playing a violin, or is it a violin playing a man? Or are they together playing the children's dreams, which are wandering through the room?

When the man takes the violin away from under his

chin and so breaks off the flow of magic, the little ones on the first tier lie with a thumb in the mouth and a contented smile on their sleepy little faces.

Good Night— Good Morning

BY TIERS THEY go to bed, and by tiers they get up in the morning; in the evening the first tier is followed by the second and then the third, and in the morning the third tier is followed by the second and the first tier. And in all that uniformity of beds and in all that uniformity of fate each child has her own questions, her own hopes, her own fears and joys, her own thoughts and her own prayers before going to sleep and upon awakening.

Good night—good morning—in those moments the children are their own beings, not a mass driven together. They will take their individuality with them, wherever they go, and only at the end and at the beginning of their day will that individuality appear.

The first tier:

The little girl who was hidden and then found sets a pious expression on her face for her bedtime prayers.

"What do you want to say: the verse of your aunts or the Jewish prayer that the other children say?"

"Both!"

She folds her little hands, closes her eyes until she can barely see, and says, just as unintelligibly as if it were Hebrew:

I-am-tired-I-want-to-go-to-sleep,-
O-God-watch-over-me-
For-give-me-I-have-sinned-
And-make-me-to-do-better.

She says it until the end, unloosens her fingers, opens her eyes, and says in the same drone, not knowing that her forefather Jacob blessed both his grandsons with it and that she is asking for the protection of his angel:

"Ha-malakh ha-goeil oti me-kol ra yivareich et ha-nearim."

Satisfied, she wriggles under the covers.

Oh, it does not matter if you do not understand any of it. It does not matter whether it is said in unintelligible Dutch or in unintelligible Hebrew. God understands all languages—if only He hears them.

Good night.

"Now I'm going to tell you a surprise—No," she says to her neighbor in the next bed—"go away. It's not for you."

With one hand protecting between the whispering mouth and the listening ear:

"You're my mommy. I'm secretly going to say mommy to you all the time. Do you think that's nice?"

"Oh—I don't think it's so nice for your own mommy, when she comes back later."

"Well," she says, and pushes her shoulders aside, "I have to have a mommy, don't I? And what if my mommy is lost?"

"Good night."

"Good night—mommy!"

He is one of the few little boys in the girls' dormitory. He is allowed to be here because his big sister is here, too.

"You were going to tell me more about God again, when I was undressed."

"I've already told you such a lot about God. What more would you like to know?"

"Oh—what He can do."

"Everything."

"He's awfully strong, isn't He? Even stronger than the boxer in father's barrack?"

"Oh, *much* stronger!"

"He can take on a hundred thousand women, can't He?"

"Well—uh—a hundred thousand women is an *awful* lot!"

"But *He* can take them on—I know it for sure. Even a million women."

"Oh."

"Say—but will God be taken away by the Germans, too?"

Good night.

"Shall we make an agreement again that you'll be dry tonight?" For the agreement has already helped a couple of times.

Not always...

"Yes. I'll be dry tonight."

She repeats it a few times because she believes that it will help better. Then she says confidentially and a bit sadly, "I was never wet at home."

"No? Why is it that you *are* wet now?"

She searches deeply within herself to find the answer to that question. Her forehead is wrinkled, and her lips are pursed. Then:

"Because it's so creepy here and strange and dark. And because the floor is so nasty and dirty."

What sort of white bed, what sort of fluffy carpet on the floor, what kind of calm light does she see behind her closed eyelids?

Good night.

The second tier:

A fight such as one that can break out only between girls; no fists and no sharp nails enter into it. Only words, which inflict pain, and answers, which feign indifference.

"Lousehead," said the girl with the blond, straight hair to her neighbor with the shaved little skull.

"I would never want to have such wisps of hair!"

"Oh, no? Didn't you used to have them? Oooo!"

"I never had such wisps of hair! I had black curls—like this!"

The sharp, dark eyes that contrast deeply with the plain gray color of the bald head indicate that she had had dark curls.

"Oh, and why are they off, then? For the fun of it, surely?"

"No, *not* for the fun of it! Because it was so filthy in the big barrack—*that's* why! As if I can help it!"

"Well—I'd never want to have such a bald lousehead!"

Suddenly when a grown-up carressingly strokes the bald head, the display of indifference is broken. From the safe protection against a shoulder that just reaches the second tier, she cries out her last defense to the enemy.

"And *I* wouldn't want to have it, either—not at all! Not at all! And you can't tease me anymore because on Tuesday I get to go on transport! Nyaah, nyaah!"

Third tier:

A German accent in a good, acquired Dutch. The two tall, grown girls lie with their heads bowed toward each other. They are looking at each other's photographs.

"That was our house. Pretty, don't you think? Mother still looked so young then. She stood behind the gate when you walked down the way."

"How long have you been away from home?"

"Six years."

"Do you still know everything? How it was exactly?"

"When I look at the photos—yes. Sometimes I don't."

"I hardly know anything anymore. When you don't even have any idea where your father and mother are..."

"Do you think that they're still alive?"

She shrugs her shoulders.

"Don't know. Does it still matter very much to you if you see them again?"

179

"Oh, I'd like to see them very much."

"Why is it that it doesn't matter to me anymore? Do you feel that way, too?"

"It still matters to me a little bit."

"Not to me. We're going to Poland, anyway."

"Maybe in Poland we'll find our families again."

Then the other girl laughs.

"Crazy kid!"

Good morning...the big girls who work in the nursery are the first to be called. The voice of the woman who calls out the names reaches through to them from a far-off distance. It takes a long time before they answer.

Very high, right under the beams of the barrack, the sleepy girls are sitting erect in their beds. They can sit up on their knees, but they cannot stand. A few of the girls possess mirrors, and they take them out from under the mattresses and carefully comb the straw from their hair. The bit of light that penetrates to the far corners from the middle of the room is enough for you to look affably at your reflection and believe that you look pretty. Those who have no mirror also believe that they look pretty. Of course, when you are fifteen, sixteen...

The girls in the second tier of beds are still lying about lazily or are playing and talking amid the straw that is raining down from the third tier.

They want very much to begin, but they are not allowed to get in the way of the big girls.

"You talked in your sleep last night!"

"Did not!"

"Did too! Don't you know that you did that?"

"Well, what did I say, then?"

"You said: iftheycome get me..."

"Well, do you have to laugh about that? Is that so crazy?"

The girls in the first tier of beds are jumping and dancing in their beds, for they are so small that they can stand up in bed.

They must wait until the big girls are there to take their clothes out from under the foot-end or the pillow and to help them. The little girls want to wait, for bed is the best place to play.

But the little girl who finds the floor nasty and dirty is still lying deep under the covers and is looking around with sad, guilty eyes. The agreement did not help; she is wet.

Good Luck Song

THE CHILDREN'S BARRACK has been closed off from the rest of the camp by a high, double barbed wire fence because a few of the children became ill with a contagious disease and were taken to the hospital. Since the time the quarantine began, the barrack has become more homelike inside. During the first days of isolation, the children and adults went about with unhappy faces. There were no visitors to the children's barrack—no one could step outside the narrow space that is so overcrowded—and then there was still the worry over the few children who seemed to be seriously ill. But then the news from the hospital barrack became more favorable, and the children and adults began to notice that you could talk with the outside world through two fences of barbed wire, although you had to shout a little, and that you could cover kilometers if only you walked industriously back and forth on your own stretch of sand inside the barbed wire. You could do exercises with large groups—get up a ball game that you never thought of doing before the quarantine—and inside, in the mess hall, you could make the evenings nice and cozy.

And there is this relief, which brings a sphere of long-forgotten peace to the barrack: Tuesdays pass by this barrack. The adults and children under quarantine cannot be sent on transport, can they! Oh, there is much good in what at first seemed to be a disaster. Each Monday afternoon from the window of the mess hall they see the train riding into the camp. Each Monday evening they see the desertion on the road because no one is allowed outside his barrack except for the guards and the few people with white armbands on. Each Tuesday morning they see the train ride away. They stand on their school tables, then, and say softly, each to himself, "Lekhu le-shalom!" Go in peace...

And yet it is as if it no longer affects them as much as it did when adults and children from their own barrack went on the train. The distance to the main road with the rails seems to have become greater. The children's barrack is like a fortress, not closed off by barbed wire, but protected by it. The weeks seem to have fewer days; from Monday morning it jumps over to Tuesday afternoon, and what happens in between is passed over. Life is good when Monday afternoon, Monday night, and Tuesday morning no longer exist.

Then on a Monday afternoon when the children are sitting at long tables under the lamp light and are eating their evening meal, the adults are called from the table to come to the corridor. The big children wink at each other as soon as the adults are gone; they have a surprise for one of the teachers, whose birthday it is, and because this is the Jewish date of her birthday, it is beginning just now, at sunset. Presently when the grown-ups come in again, all the children will stand up—the little ones above on the benches—and together they will sing, "Mazeltov! Mazeltov!" Good luck...good luck...

But in the corridor stands a messenger who has penetrated the infectious barrack to bring the bad news: early tomorrow the quarantine will be lifted, for a half-day, and it will be resumed tomorrow afternoon. The barbed wire gates will be open to let out those children who will be going on transport. The commandant has said that the children's barrack has remained out of reach for too long. Besides, from where else must the thousands of people be taken in order to fill the train? The well is running dry.

"Many children?" they ask, their lips pale.

The messenger nods. The others do not dare to ask the number.

"Specific groups?"

The messenger nods again. He waits a moment before he imparts the information.

"Only the children who have no parents here."

The adults avoid one another's gazes. Each one is thinking about the few children who have become closer to him than the others. But they are all thinking about the little children who are here without parents. The big children—perhaps they will come through it all right. But the little ones...

Thank you," says an adult hoarsely. For they do not have to know more.

Guiltily they steal back to the mess hall.

One wink from the big boy, and the little children climb up on the benches and hold each other by the hand in order not to fall. The other children stand up, their shining, laughing eyes directed toward the teacher whose birthday it is.

Then a song breaks, a song that pierces through the roof of the children's barrack, through the evening air, right to the sky. The children's voices are powerful and high and clear, and their jubilations are supported by the low voices of the big boys.

Mazeltov! Mazeltov!
Mazeltov! Mazeltov!

Good luck...good luck...good luck...

How Can Herod
Bear the Light*

IN THE NIGHT, after a couple hours of rest, the grown-ups arise quietly and slink toward the mess hall, shivering.

The list has come.

They read it silently. By a few of the names comes a stifled "oh!" or a sob. They may still express their feelings now; presently, when they are helping the children pack or are dressing the little ones or getting food packages ready, there cannot be any cries, not even stifled ones, and there can be no sobbing, either. For the little children must believe in a way out, and the big children must believe in their chance for a future. But then these adults, who are now standing together, helpless and defeated, will be helped by their own working hands, their own running feet.

Each one goes back to the dormitory that is *his* dormitory, where the children have become *his* children. Each one has counted how many there are on the list from his own dormitory; there are many—oh, it is *more* than the dormitory can bear. There will be empty beds tomorrow and the day after tomorrow—and then new children will be brought into the camp, and the beds will be used again, but what good is that? These children have become their own children, and they are going to be dragged from their arms. Where to? Where to? If only there were enough hope...

Before the bigger children are awakened, that sobbing must stop. It must. It must. You are allowed to be torn

---

*The title is from a Christmas song in seventeenth-century Dutch, "O Kerstnacht, Schooner dan de Daegen," text by Joost van den Vondel, melody by Dirk Sweelinck (?): "O Christmas night, more beautiful than the days, / How can Herod bear the light, / Which illuminates your darkness and is celebrated and adored? / His pride listens to no reason, / However shrill it sounds in his ears."—Translators

apart from the inside, as long as it remains invisible. You must have the strength and the composure to awaken them when it is morning and time to get up. You must compose yourself. You must. Oh, there is no getting away from it.

"I'm still so tired..."

"Darling, you must get up. You really must get up."

The big girl suddenly sits erect, her eyes wide open.

"Do I have to get up? Is it still night? Is it Monday night?"

"Yes."

"I don't want to! I don't want to!" she shouts, and you stifle her cry against your shoulder. The other children whose names are not on the list must not awaken, and those whose names are on the list must be awakened gently, not by a cry of distress. You stroke her hair that is lying on your shoulder and say some foolish words that do not help and do not change anything. And when the twisted little face is lifted from your shoulder and the young hands are resigned and begin to do what must be done before she is taken away, you climb down from the high bed in order to climb up to another high bed and rouse another girl from her sleep.

This is your work: to disturb sleep, the unconscious sleep of girls, and to make those girls conscious of a reality that is unbearable. This is your work: to smother cries against your shoulder and then to continue on and disturb another girl's sleep.

Then you awaken the younger children, who must still be helped. They are swathed in many clothes, and while they are being dressed they merely stand there, sleepy and dazed. They knew that this would come one day—only not yet. Oh, well, another time or now—but they are still so tired...

A little girl who is six understands as soon as she opens her eyes. Wildly she kicks her covers away, screams, and keeps screaming...

185

"Oh, mommy, mommy! I don't want to go to Poland!"

But mommy is somewhere else in the world—perhaps in Poland already—perhaps she is no longer somewhere else in the world—and mommy would not be able to help her, even if her little girl's cry brought her to the children's barrack at this moment. In any case, this time it is only the children without mothers who are being sent off. But how can mommy single out her little girl's cry when the world is so full of children's cries—children's cries for help that does not come?

In the boys' dormitory the big boys go about with white, grim faces. Those who must go away pack their things together and ask for and receive the most necessary items that they are lacking. Those who do not have to go quietly ask what they can do to help. The big girls who do not have to go away help, too, and act just like little mothers as they dress the little children. They search for their escape by being busy, both those who are remaining and those who are leaving. The boys write names on rucksacks and food bowls; they look for shoe laces, do not find them, lace the shoes with paper strings. They give each other advice while they pack. If those faces were not so white and grim, it would seem like the preparation for a picnic. But each one who goes bustling about knows that this is the preparation for a trip upon which their thoughts are fixed. Each boy knows it—and each is silent.

The little boys, even more clumsy than the little girls, wait docilely until someone helps them. A few laugh brightly through the silence because they look so fat in all that underclothing. The laughter then catches hold of the other little boys, too. They look at one another and laugh at one another, and they begin to believe in an adventure. The word "transport," which was frightening up until now, is no longer fearful now that it has come close to them. They are the word itself, those who are going on transport; they themselves will be there. They will finally discover what it means.

The babies and the little children are taken from their beds as soon as a small rucksack has been prepared for each of them. They are sleeping—perhaps somewhat fitfully because of the bustling in the big dormitory—and they know nothing. The word "transport" exists only for the biggest children among them. It is a borrowed word, a word without meaning. It is a word that is like "punishment." They have done nothing naughty—who is thinking about punishment?

Some of the children have their temperatures taken. There are a few sick ones—who knows, perhaps they will be lucky and have a fever above 103°! Under that is no good. Actually it must be 104°, but 103° is cause for hope...

The little two-year-old boy who is always doubled over in bed with his head on his knees because in the previous camp he did not get any milk and thus became very weak, receives the thermometer without awakening. Tense, anxious faces look for the line of mercury that is going to decide his fate. No one can find it before the thermometer is taken out.

He cannot bring it up past 96°, he really cannot.

From where is he to draw the strength to be feverish? He has lost it long ago. He can never become warm—he really cannot—oh, let him alone...96° does not count. A cold, weak little child does not count. If this bit of warmth, this bit of strength, this bit of life should slip away from him—well, then he would count. But then another little child would have to go in his place, in order to fill the quota. Perhaps it is better this way, for it is such a very small bit of life. Presently in the cattle car, when he is cared for by someone who by chance takes pity on him, then perhaps that little bit of life will slip away from him, and then no other little child will have to go in his place. It really is better this way...

In the mess hall the blackout has ended because the day, the Tuesday, is slowly beginning to break. The room is full of rucksacks with names and birth dates written on them, full of packages and food bowls. The children sit on the benches and wait, thickly clothed and moving uncomfortably. They drink milk and eat bread upon which the jam has been spread extra thick, and the younger children no longer mind it so much. The bigger children maintain a front of careless high spirits for each other and for the little ones. They are hungry from the wakeful night, and eagerly they bite into the unusually delicious bread with their young teeth. If they can keep up the front for a long time, they will forget about the reality; they want to do that very much.

But when the guard comes, his face taut because he may not think about what his weekly task has become—then suddenly the front recedes. This man is real. He is coming to take them.

No farewells—oh, no farewells and don't cry so, you big girls...Don't bite on your lips like that, you big boys—it's better to cry, then...Oh, and can't that little boy stop calling for his mother, who isn't there?...And won't that line ever stop? Will everything be empty? Is this the end?

They look back and wave at the children's barrack. But the little ones, wrapped in blankets and carried on the arm, let themselves be sent away like inert packages.

Don't wave, oh, don't wave so...

And don't look back...

4. Star Hell

Passage to Hell

THERE IS GREAT, joyous excitement in the camp: an empty passenger train has arrived! The first ones who saw it shouted out in disbelief and surprise. They called to the others; each person who was able went to the main road to see if it were true.

Those who could not come because of work or illness laughed at the others and said that it might be another nice story, just as so many that arise, blossom, and then die away. But when it persisted, and the workers who were finished with their work confirmed it too, everyone had to believe it.

Now even nicer tales are rising out of the ground: bread and cigarettes and apples are being loaded in—the Red Cross is behind it. This transport will be exchanged for German prisoners and will be treated with respect and care. They will first go to a camp with brick barracks and without forced labor—another month or so and the people with papers for Palestine will be on their way to Palestine, those with English papers on their way to England, those with purchased Honduras papers on their way to...well, not to the Honduras, for that is a bit far if you have never been there before and at most have only looked it up in an atlas.

You don't believe it? And that passenger train, then? Isn't that unbelievable and yet true? Then other unbelievable things can happen, too, can't they?

The people walk back and forth along the passenger cars just as they do on Monday evening when they walk back and forth along the cattle cars. A German official has come by herself to the camp to decide who shall be considered as exchange prisoners. She has called in people to see their papers, and some received a summons to be transported to an exchange camp. Those who did were congratulated, and they received the congratulations with laughter. This time it is not their imagination; they are to be sent by a passenger train—isn't that proof that they are riding to meet their good fortune?

And the children who went with father and mother to the German official and who later received a letter shouted out in excitement. They dream of apples and bread and sugar and sweets and sausage, for everyone has been talking about it, even though no one has seen that kind of food loaded into the train. Who says that they will not have a little house together with father and mother in that other camp? You don't know; if they are planning to exchange you for their own men, they must be careful with you. Tomorrow—tomorrow the train will leave! Today people are still being summoned to the German official, and perhaps more will be called tomorrow. There are some who had at first chosen to remain here because they had a good chance of not being sent to Poland; now that they have seen the passenger train with their own eyes, they are trying to be allowed to approach the German woman to ask if they can still go...

But in the morning the privileged who work near the German woman and who have toiled through the night relate that there was a long and vehement telephone conversation between her and her superiors and that the trip to the wonder camp, the trip by passenger train, has been postponed for an indefinite period...Most of the people do not unpack their suitcases. They cannot believe that from one day to another a dream is being destroyed. The children walk past the train that actually has doors and windows and seats inside, and they are too unhappy for tears. How can that be? But perhaps it is just a rumor; the train is still there...

In the afternoon the train rides away, empty. When the people in the camp can see the rails running smooth and straight along the main road again, they begin to believe that they have been dreaming an absurd, unreal, bold dream, a dream of riding in a car intended for people, complete with seats. People certainly can have crazy dreams! And it was such a strange, mass dream in which everyone awakened at the same time...How odd...

Seven weeks later the German woman is back in the camp. No one believes the rumor anymore, and those who do believe it no longer want to. Even when the passenger train comes into the camp again, the prisoners point at it mockingly, and the conversation is full of sick jokes. The children look at it suspiciously and think that it might immediately ride away again.

But the train does not ride away. It remains, waiting for them. Only the rumors about apples and cigarettes are not discussed; bread *has* been loaded into the train, for some have actually seen that happen.

They may take as much baggage with them as they wish, and money, too, if they still have some. The money, which had to be turned in when they came to the camp, is returned to some of the prisoners. Is this a fairy tale?

The people who are driven to the train are not the defeated, dull, silent herds this time. There is talking and laughter; those remaining behind may not go outside, but from inside the barracks they wave and call out to them to have a pleasant journey. The personal loads appear light; the heavy, cumbersome pieces of baggage, which the guards put on wheelbarrows and brought to the train, were handed over with trust. Presently those pieces might appear out of the formless heap—presently, in the wonder camp with brick barracks and without forced labor. In former days when you entrusted your baggage to the luggage vans, didn't you also not know what would happen to it later? Then the adults and children are shoved hurriedly into the cars. There are many more people than there are places. But when they have made room for themselves and have put their loads in the racks or have set them on the floor, the big suitcases from the wheelbarrows are shoved inside through the open windows. Chests and suitcases and bags are stacked high in the room between the seats intended for the legs of the passengers. It has to be, shout the guards, for there is no baggage car, and otherwise the large pieces cannot go along. The adults look at each other silently and try to place their legs somewhere between the bundles. In their excitement the children read the names that are written on the suitcases and squat above on the seats or search for a place on top of the baggage. The young people, brimming with happiness at the thought of going to Palestine, had planned this morning to sing Hebrew songs as soon as the train began to depart, just as the young people in the cattle cars did on their way to Poland. But when the train actually begins to leave, they are still trying to find a place to put their legs and thus forget to sing the Hebrew songs; they forget, the very people who are riding in a passenger train on their way to Palestine— the very people who are not in a cattle car on their way to Poland. When they realize it they are ashamed, but by then it is too late; the camp is behind them now and could no longer hear the singing that it hears each week with such admiration and pride when the cattle cars depart. And the legs, there is no room for those miserable legs— yet they have dreamed so of a triumphant departure...

Goodbye, Holland—goodbye, dear Holland—this is our farewell: in the falling darkness but with the moon- light shining carefully and gently over the winter heather, shining over the quiet, faithful forests, over the last, dis- persed houses. Goodbye, Holland—you did not want the departure to be like this, without our own free will being able to determine the moment, without a hand being able to reach out to touch you for the last time.

The children do not say their farewells. They have

not had the experience of enough years to feel bonded to this country that is now being pushed away from them under the wheels of the dark train. They have never had time to put roots down somewhere in the world. Perhaps that is good; pulling up roots is painful, and breaking off the end of the root leaves a wound. Without pain and without a wound the children ride to that country which rules over them.

When they become sleepy, they begin nagging for bread and sweets. There is just enough moonlight coming inside so that the mothers can crawl from their cramped positions to fetch their bags with food.

Most of them received packages shortly before the departure, and these come in handy now. When the children are satisfied, they nestle above on the stacks of baggage and try to sleep. The little ones must lie in their mothers' arms, but there is no space for mothers' arms, and how can they have a lap when there is no place for their legs? This is a passenger car; how did the mothers in the cattle cars do it? And how did the little ones in the cattle cars do it, the little ones who had no mother who at least *tried* to make a lap? And how did they manage on the second night, and the third?

In the clear moonlight the adults see the land rolling by and large bodies of water where lonely farms and isolated groups of trees protrude above them. Sometimes the train stands still for hours somewhere in the country, without a city or a station. When the engine begins to pull the train again, the children are awakened with a start but go back to sleep right away; they know where they are and are calm: they are sitting with father and mother in the train, on their way to Palestine...

The train stops again, someplace where a big city must have been. Through a barren space along which scorched, blackened beams indicate where houses and a street have been, a tram is riding, absurd and grotesque. Is the moon playing along in this game of death? Then why is it lighting the open hollows so sharply among the black stakes? Why is it causing the glass that remains in the charred window frames to glitter so white? And as the train goes farther, why does the moon come along and display the dead city from the one end to the other? The children remain sleeping while riding through this ghostly world. The adults look at each other, silent and shivering. In each other's eyes they are reading the same words of the damned that the great, mighty hand has written above the charred remains of houses, across the starry skies: "Menei menei tekeil u-farsin." They feel no joy that this was the city of the enemy; they feel no pity that these were the homes of its people. They know only that for a moment the blindfold has been taken from their mortal eyes and that they are seeing the end of a world rolling past them.

But the little girl who has been put down to sleep in the corner by a window and whose eyes seem to be closed says in a high, emphatic voice, "Is this Palestine? I don't want to live in Palestine because all the houses are broken here!"

For half the night the train stands still on a deserted track. They take turns sleeping. When they awaken and see that they have not yet gone any farther, they are resigned to the thought that perhaps they will be left here, forgotten forever. But when the day dawns, the pulling of the engine jolts everyone awake. Through forests and heaths they approach the camp. Tired and dazed they no longer believe that there will be brick barracks and that the Red Cross will watch over them.

When the train stops again and they are driven out with short, biting commands—and when they are awaited by a row of heavily armed men in uniforms, whose insignia and symbol is a death's head—and when they see the bread, which was loaded into the train in the previous camp, now lying on the ground in a careless heap—and when those who are able to walk or stumble along in rows of five must begin the two-hour-long march to the camp—then they know better.

The little children with their mothers, the invalids and the seriously ill must wait to be transported by trucks.

The mothers sit on the ground or on their suitcases with their babies in their arms. When the truck comes, they are immediately loaded into it; they must stretch their arms out to take their little ones, for otherwise another person would be loaded in on top of the child. It must be done quickly. When the truck is completely full, without room for movement, the tailgate is closed with an iron bolt, and the truck rides away. There is not a single opening in the wooden sides; not a single beam of light is shining inside. A riding, jolting darkness has swallowed up the mothers and children. The mothers call that here a small child is standing, to warn others not to step on it. They hold the babies in their arms and the little children between their knees, but they do not know whether it is their own children that they feel moving there and whose frightened little fists are grabbing them. The children are screaming in fear and dismay. None of the mothers can discern her own child's voice from all the raucous little voices, no mother knows where to reach her own child to comfort it.

Then, above these cries of despair, a mother suddenly begins to sing:

> Three little children
> Were sitting on a fence,
> On top of a fence...

A short silence falls amid the screaming. Then more mothers sing along, and then the children, clear and unconcerned. When the song is over, another one immediately begins, then another. And so a singing darkness rides over the Lüneburg heath. A truck is riding, fully loaded with children's songs. Then the truck stops with a rough jerk. The bolt is shoved back and the tailgate is lowered, so that the eyes are blinded and the limbs are paralyzed in the jamming of the others. The last song is not yet over, so the children sing it until the end.

The men in uniforms with the death's heads stand in front of them and guard them so that no one escapes. They are greeted with children's song.

"Come on! Hurry!" calls one.

For they are in a hurry. Oh, God, they are in such a hurry...

Nights

SHE SLEPT VERY, very deeply on the first night; she was *so* tired from the previous night in the train and from standing outside for the whole day next to father while waiting for their names to be written down. Her mother and little sister had come into camp in a truck, and their names had been taken down long before. She was tired from unpacking and from making her bed, so tired that she could hardly eat what mother had prepared for her in the meantime, so tired that she climbed up immediately into her top bunk. On that first night she did not get out of her bed even once, and that almost never happens to her in a camp, for in the barrack there are always children who are crying, or women who are calling out to one another, or someone who is unwell or who falls out of a top bed. Then you wake up, and when you are awake, right away you have to go to the bathroom—she does, at least. You usually go back to sleep quickly, but if there are three or more times that you have made that long trip through the narrow passageways between the beds and waited by the bathroom until it was free, and then walked back again— then you certainly are very tired the next morning! And on that morning after the first night she was hardly tired, she had slept so soundly.

On the second night she did have to get up, but at least there was a bit of light on in the dormitory. It was a good thing, too, because the passageways here are much narrower than in the previous camp; fat women have to walk sideways, otherwise they cannot get through, and mothers with small children in their arms must twist and turn to make sure that the child does not bump its head. At night there are also little stools in the passageways because some women cannot climb down from a top bunk without one. If there is a little bit of light, and if you look carefully, then you will not bump yourself too badly on the way to the bathroom.

And the third night was the night with that mother of the two little children who now sleeps beneath her. The littlest one is over a year old, and yet it still drinks from its mother; the mother says that this is the only milk that she can count on, for she does not know if the children will continue to receive milk here. The first two nights she slept with the children on a couple of benches in the mess hall; there are separate mess halls in the barracks here, with tables and benches and stools, and people always fight for places at mealtime because there is not enough room. There was no lower bunk left over for this mother with the children, and you cannot sleep in a top bunk with such little children because they would naturally fall out of it. Big children like her belong in the top bunks, and women without children, if they are not too old, at least, to climb up to them. But under her on those first two nights slept two young girls, adults, really, and they did not want to give up their beds for a mother with children. It was terribly mean of them, for as a result the mother with those little children had to sleep on benches in the mess hall.

It was on the third night, late in the evening and with everyone already sleeping, when that mother went mad, surely because of fatigue. For before those two nights she had sat up all during that night in the train, with no room for her legs, and with those two children with her. Suddenly a screaming voice came through the dormitory, which frightened her terribly and which she did not immediately understand because she was not yet wide awake. "Three nights without sleep! Even an animal gets straw to lie on! I shall have a bed! My children shall have a bed! If I don't sleep on this night, no one in this barrack shall sleep! I'm going crazy! I'm going *crazy!* Do you hear me? Do you all hear me? Not *one* person in the whole barrack shall close her eyes if I do not get a bed for myself and my children!"

The women near her knew about those two young girls who were lying comfortably in two bottom beds and who did not want to get out of them. They called to those two that they should be ashamed of themselves and that they must make room for that mother. But those two girls snarled back that they should mind their own business and that they did not intend to move at eleven o'clock at night. And all throughout that calling and snarling the voice of the mother was screaming, "Not *one* shall sleep! I must have a bed!"

Then another mother, who has a small child herself and lies in a bottom bunk, came to the two girls. She did not call out or shout. She came to one of the beds and sat down on the edge of it. She talked very softly, just as you talk when you sit cozily on the edge of someone's bed. At first the two snarled back, but when they received only quiet answers, they had to speak softly back to her.

"Of course," she heard the other mother say, "we are all a bit on edge. But I'll help you move. With the three of us it'll be done in no time."

The young girl was lying quietly in her bed above them. She had the feeling that a warm stream was going through her whole body. She was *so* happy that this could still happen, even here: talking softly and encouraging the other to talk softly, too. When the girls underneath her had gotten out of their beds and had begun to move their things, she looked over the edge of her bed; everything was going very quietly and quickly, and the mother with the two little children had stopped screaming because they had reassured her that she would get a bed.

Later that other mother helped make up the beds for those three, and she tucked them all in; she remained for a while, talking. The young girl above them lay there and listened and thought that never in a camp had she been so happy.

But the forth night is *so* terrible that all the good of the previous night appears to be forgotten, just as if it has subsided into all the wretchedness and horror of the day and night that followed.

Everything in the bathroom is stopped up; you walk through the filthy water, you cannot wash, and the toilet cannot be used. It can never be used during the day, but at night it is necessary to do so because you cannot leave the barrack and because it is a ten-minute walk to those nasty little houses. The people themselves cannot help that everything has been stopped up; they are all new here, and they do not yet know how badly built everything is. But the men in green uniforms say that it is because they are so dirty and so lazy. All Jews are dirty and lazy, they say, and it is time for them to be broken of that. They do not *say* it— they shout it, with many ugly words that you never learned in your German lessons at school. They shout, too, that for punishment the bathroom will now be closed for a week. Water must then be hauled from the men's camp. For a few hours a bathroom will be open for them there so that they can haul water. And for the rest they must use the latrine, day and night. During this time, they will not be shot at when they go outside the barrack at night. This is terrible for mother and for all the mothers with little children. They lend each other buckets and jugs for hauling water, and the bigger children, such as she, quickly drag back as much water as possible for as long as that bathroom in the men's camp is open to them. It is ten minutes there and certainly fifteen minutes back when you are carrying such a heavy jug of water; your feet sink deeply into the mud when you have something so heavy to drag. How wicked it is, really, first to make it so that you are unable to wash yourself and then to say that you are dirty. She never knew in the previous camp that the men in green were so bad.

And then night comes. For the sick, the elderly women, and the children there is an old, empty bucket set up in the mess hall, and by turns there is someone keeping watch. If a woman who does not have her own flashlight must go to the latrine, she receives a small flashlight that you must press continually with your thumb in order to get a little bit of light.

Then it happens that the lights all over the camp go out because there is something wrong with the blackout system. Now she will first have to find her way in the dark through the barrack, through the narrow little path with the stools—she will have to count the beds on the way back so that she will not climb into the wrong one— and then with the little flashlight she will have to go the long, long way through the mud and look for the latrine. She is becoming sick with fear just thinking about it; she knows that she will have to make that trip often, and she therefore goes to bed with her clothes on. She does not share her troubles with mother, who has enough difficulties with the little sister and with no water. If only she could fib and say that she is not yet twelve years old— then she could go to the mess hall! But she is thirteen and a very tall girl.

Her coat is lying at the foot-end. When she awakens late in the evening and feels that she must get up, all she has to do is put on her coat and her stockings before she lets herself down in the dark. Under the bottom bed she gropes for her shoes that fortunately she finds quickly. Then, feeling her way out with her one hand and counting the beds with her other, she finds her way to the mess hall. She bumps herself a few times against the stools, but now she knows immediately where they are for the return trip.

In the mess hall the woman keeping watch luckily has been able to get a light that burns permanently without going out. She still hopes that the woman will think she is a child under twelve, but the woman immediately hands her the flashlight. It is very difficult to use; you must press it strongly and quickly, otherwise it will not give off any light at all.

And then, shivering, she is standing in the cold, in the dark, in the mud.

She presses the light as fast as she can and she sees

just a bit of the path between the barracks. She must take care to stay in the middle, for along the barracks are deep trenches, and she does not want to end up in them. It becomes more difficult when the barracks end and when you must cross the large field to the latrine; when you have nothing on either side of you, it is easy to lose your sense of direction. There is no moon at all.

Now and then when she steps in a mud puddle she forgets to press on the flashlight, and then she misses that small, weak little beam of light. Not that the little beam of light helps much in so large a field! In order to know how to cross the field to find the latrine you would have to have a glimmer of light over the whole field. But she believes a little bit that she is feeling the direction and that she is crossing straight over.

Suddenly there is no ground anymore; she has fallen down into a ditch. Obviously she had not been walking straight ahead. She cannot get up, and she does not want to, either. She has forgotten why she had begun the trip. Now she wants only to remain lying there throughout the entire cold night and wait until morning when it is light again. It does not matter to her anymore.

Then the searchlight from the watchtower turns toward her side. She sees the edge of the trench and a large section of the field; nearby she sees the latrine. While the searchlight is still pointed in her direction, she climbs out and walks quickly toward it. Her heart is beating wildly from climbing and also from the fear that perhaps that man in the watchtower above does not know that she is permitted to leave the barrack at night. He would shoot at her, then. Oh, well—and *if* he shoots? It doesn't really matter anymore. In the latrine she does not have her hands free to press on the light. She puts it in her coat pocket and gropes to find her way. During the day, you can see where it is dirty and where it isn't. Now she sees nothing, and it is dirty.

On the way back the searchlight flashes one more time over her, and through that she knows where the barracks are, and between the barracks it goes better. Through a crack in the door she sees the lights shining in the mess hall and thus she finds the way inside. Another person is already waiting impatiently for the flashlight.

"You've certainly been gone a long time!" says the woman who is keeping watch.

"Yes," she says dully. She cannot talk about everything that was outside there; it is too awful. She only stammers hoarsely, "I'm sick. I'm really sick. May I stay inside next time?"

By the light of the lamp the woman examines her face, upon which all the horror and mud is stamped, and nods. She writes her name down for the following watch. When she has counted the beds in the dormitory and has again bumped herself against the stools, she pulls off her wet, muddy shoes and climbs up. She lays her soaking-wet coat at the foot-end once more.

She wants to sleep. Oh, she wants only to sleep. Soon when she must come down again, she is sick, thank goodness, and only has to go in the dark to the mess hall. She will no longer fall into a trench, she will not be shot dead again. She will no longer have to go into that dirty latrine where you cannot see but only feel...

After a few hours she awakens, damp in her outergarments. She must reflect a bit; why are they so wet? It is only sweat—it is fortunately only sweat.

She lets herself down and feels her way in the dark to the mess hall.

Roll Call

THOSE WHO MUST go to work do not go to their roll call; they have already been herded out of their barrack at six in the morning to report to the workers' roll call. Those who are sick and have a temperature above 103°—below 103° does not count at all—must still leave at six to report to sick call; no one else may do it for them, for the men in green uniforms do not trust that. From work call they then go in rows of five to their work: most report to the tent for shoes, where they must tear old shoes apart. Many men report to outside work, where they must dig or pull manure carts in place of horses. Many women report to the kitchen to peel potatoes and to clean vegetables. You see them going out by the barrack gate in long trains that seem to have no end. After half-past eleven you see them coming back, at least if everything is all right and they are not being punished by having to work until six o'clock without rest or food. As soon as they are in the barrack, at a quarter to twelve, they storm into the eating area; they are in a terrible hurry, for they must first wait in line for their food, then find a place at one of the tables, then quickly swallow their meal—and if they are mothers, they must also feed the children—then go into the bathroom to wash the plate under the tap, and then at half-past twelve they are herded out of the barrack again for the midday work call.

If they do not have to work an extra hour as punishment, then after six o'clock you see them coming back again. The men quickly try to go to the barrack where their wives and children are and eat their bread with them. They must hurry, for at seven o'clock the men must be out of the women's camp. If they are punished with an extra hour's work, then of course they cannot go to the women's camp at all.

But that is the day of the workers. *Their* day—hers and grandmother's and grandfather's, too—is very different. Their roll call is different, too.

Grandfather and grandmother do not have to report to work because they are over sixty-five. She herself does not have to because she is under fifteen. She lives in the barrack with grandmother, for she has no one else. Father and mother were hidden separately, and she was captured and father and mother were not. Fortunately she was permitted to come here on grandfather's Palestine papers, otherwise she would have been sent to Poland without anyone. Now she sleeps in the bed above grandmother.

At nine in the morning they are warned to report to the big roll call field. The roll call itself is conducted by a man in green uniform. It is not until ten o'clock that all the prisoners from the barracks are standing at their places; they have already been counted by the barrack leaders, and they have had much to do before reporting to the field. Before you leave the barrack you must wash your mug and plate from breakfast and make your bed. It is no ordinary bed making, such as you do at home. All your belongings must be put away in it, and yet it must appear flat and straight, just as if no one lived in it. Here it is called bed building, and it is very difficult. You are punished severely if there is something wrong with it, and if there are many beds in a barrack that are not made correctly, then the whole barrack is punished—the margarine and jam are withheld for a week, or the barrack leader must sit in a cubicle called a bunker. The men in green can at any time hold an inspection while you are standing at roll call, thus it must be in order before you go out the door.

The purpose of the roll call is to count all the thousands of people in the camp, every day. The men in green want to know if anyone has run away; as if you could, with all those tenfold electric barbed wires with death's heads painted on them and with all those watchtowers and guns! Yet the men in green are always afraid that someone will run away. The workers have already been counted in the morning, and now all the barrack groups on the field are counted, and the sick and the very old and the mothers of children under three years old, who may remain inside, are counted in the barracks, and the sick people in the hospital are counted in their beds, and then everything is added up together, and if it tallies, then roll call is over. But it never tallies, and therefore it sometimes lasts for hours. If you are dead before roll call begins, then you no longer count, but if you are busy dying then you still count. It is the same with being born; if you are born before the roll call, then you count, but if you are busy being born, naturally you don't. That makes it all very complicated. Actually, everyone knows that the men in green let the number tally if they are in a good mood and that they let it be one too few or too many if they are angry and want to harass you. There was one day when they stood at roll call for eight hours, in the rain and the mud. The workers who came back to their barracks at midday also had to form a group on the roll call field and from there had to return to their work without eating. That was certainly the worst day. It happened because the commandant was away on a trip, and the other men in green wanted to show what they could do in the commandant's absence. Many people became very sick then, and that time marked the beginning of many deaths among the older people.

If the sun is shining and roll call is not long—an hour or so—then it is not so unpleasant. Before you must go stand in groups, you meet your friends from other barracks, and you talk a little with them. When you must stand still but there is not yet an officer on the field, you sing songs together. The women tell each other wonderful recipes from the time when there was not yet a war and when they could cook in their own kitchens. Talking about delicious food helps when you are hungry; it is just as if you are actually eating it. But when a man in green uniform is coming in the distance, they are warned of it, and then suddenly it is deathly still. There must be no talking. Small children do not understand that, and they continue with their talk and laughter. Once their barrack had to stand for an extra hour because the children were not quiet. Across from them stand those in the men's barracks. Grandfather is there, too. As soon as the man in green walks past them, the men must take off their hats or their caps. "Caps off!" is then commanded by the barrack leader.

Grandfather has such pretty, white hair, and such a fine head with such a high forehead. Each time that he uncovers that hair and that forehead and bows for the officer who comes by, she thinks the same thing:

"Not so low, grandfather—oh, not so low!"

Whether the roll call lasts for a long time or a short

time, the whistle that the Jewish overseer of the camp blows, the whistle that means "it's over!" always comes unexpectedly. You always try to count on the fact that roll call might never end; therefore it always turns out better than you expected. Then you run back to your barrack with the other children, and you wave and wink through the windows at those who have remained inside, "It's over!" Every day it is a new pleasure, that each roll call is over at last, even though it has taken such a long time.

It is dark and stormy today. Heavy, gray clouds pass over the roll call field, and now and then the rain falls in torrents. All the prisoners have their collars up and cloths or caps over their faces. It *would* have to take such a long time today. When the man in green uniform walks past the barrack group to count them, the barrack leader takes one step forward and asks, in the flat tone that you must use when speaking to a man in green, whether that one old woman may be brought to the hospital, for if she is not supported by others, she will fall.

The man in green does not even look to see which woman it is who is almost falling.

"She will remain standing—even if she should fall dead!" he shouts.

He walks through toward the next group.

But you are used to the men in green, and you can no longer feel...

From her place she can just see the hospital barrack. Every day she sees a man in green go into the hospital to count, and after a while she sees him come out again. Sometimes she sees an empty manure cart riding by. It is pulled by a horse, and a man in green is in the driver's seat. That means that there has been a death, or several deaths. During roll call the coffins are carried to the gate of the hospital and are loaded onto the cart. Then the tailgate is pushed closed behind it, and the man in green drives the cart away. This is the only manner in which horses are used; all the other kinds of loads in the manure carts are pulled by men.

Because of the storm and the torrential rains, there

are naturally many deaths today; that is what happens when the dark clouds come. Engrossed, she sees how a heavy coffin is carried outside and shoved onto the cart. The men carrying it go back and return a bit later with another coffin. Thus it is two...or even more?

With difficulty they shove the second coffin on top of the first; it was placed lopsided. The tailgate will have to hold it back...

But before the tailgate is put up against it, suddenly the whistle blows; roll call is over. The children run away, shouting, and do not see what she has seen: that the second coffin is still not sitting well and that the tailgate has not yet been placed against it.

The horse, frightened by the running, noisy children, throws his head back and bolts. Into the dark, wild day, he bolts...

She sees it happening and cannot move. She holds her hands in front of her mouth, above which her eyes watch in bewilderment at what certainly will happen: the coffin on top will be hurled off...

In front of the outermost gate the man in green sitting on the cart has the reins in his hands again. The horse comes to a stop and nothing happens.

But when grandfather comes past her, she grasps his arm with clenched fingers and smothers her desperate scream against his wet sleeve.

Hunger

AT HOME YOU were never allowed to look at the plate of another to see if he had more than you. You simply could not do that.

Here you do it automatically. When there are four unpeeled potatoes for everyone, you wonder if you will get two large ones and two small ones, or four small ones. You always think that you are receiving less than another person intentionally. When all the children of that mother at the table next to yours have a couple of large potatoes, then that must have been intentional, mustn't it? And when other children show you the little pieces of meat that they have fished out of their turnips, why is it, then, that you yourself have almost never come across a piece of meat?

Mother keeps saying that you may not look at another person's plate, not even in a camp and not even when you are hungry. But she is silent when she cannot give you even one piece of meat and when she lays a few small potatoes on your plate; thus he knows for sure that she has looked at the plate of another who had more.

"Everyone is lucky sometime," she sighs. How would she know that other people were lucky, if she had not looked at their plates? He knows all about it, all right!

They have not peeled their potatoes for a long time now; there is always a bit left on the peels, and to throw that out would be sinful. But looking in the garbage can to see if anyone has thrown any food away—he does not do that yet. That really is a bit dirty. It is better to wait near the garbage barrel. Sometimes there is food that you think some people cannot swallow because it has a lot of twigs in it. Then if you see someone going to the garbage barrel with a plate, you hurry to him and ask if you may have it. In that way you can receive an extra portion once in a while.

If there are portions of food left over, they are divided among the people whose turn it is for an extra morsel. Every day he looks at the list to see if it is their turn. He cannot help but look, even if he knows that they have just had a turn and that it will not come again for a long time. Still, you never can tell, can you?

Sometimes big men have the job of lugging the heaviest cauldrons of food to the barracks. The ordinary cauldrons are carried by the women themselves. Such men are usually clever enough to carry a mug at their belt; if the barrack leader is just a little bit nice, she will give them half a mug of soup as a present for bringing the food. There is one old man here who used to live in a large, splendid house. He used to always pass it on his way to school, and that is how he knows the man. This old man carries cauldrons and asks for a bit of soup in *such* a polite manner that not *one* of the barrack leaders can say no. It is not permitted, really, for the portions are measured out precisely for the people in the barrack, but just one bite can certainly be given. How lucky it is to carry the cauldrons and to be able to ask so politely!

There is another way to get more food, and that is to lick the cauldrons. The children in the barrack are given turns to lick them, thus your turn does come once in a while. But in some barracks where there are no children, the cauldrons are not licked out very well. They are set outside, empty, but they are not really that empty. You know the place where all the empty cauldrons are set before they are taken outside the gate. You look inside all the cauldrons, and if there is still something in them, you scrape them with the spoon that you have brought with you, or with your fingers. The only thing is, there are other children who know that trick, thus you must be an early bird!

And yet with all those little tricks, he remains empty and hollow inside. Mother does not have anymore yarn or clothes that she can exchange for bread; all their clothes are needed, many of them are already worn out, and there is no more yarn for darning them. Where are you to get extra food?

He is in a strange barrack, looking for a friend from the lessons. In the afternoons they have lessons in groups. This is not actually permitted, for they must not learn anything, but the teachers pretend to merely keep them busy, in the meantime teaching them quite a lot. They may not call it "school" or "lessons"; "club" is the only word that is permitted. He has made a friend at these lessons, a very nice boy who is the same age as he. It is a shame that they do not live in the same barrack.

He looks through the mess hall but does not see him. He goes into the dormitory, past all the rows of beds, and calls his name. Tired and disappointed, he returns to the mess hall.

On the barrack leaders' table are the bread portions, already sliced and ready to be distributed. The leaders themselves are not there. There are some women at the other tables, mothers of little children who do not have to work. They are very busy with their children or with darning or sewing. A couple of women in the corner of the mess hall are quarreling, and their screams can be heard all the way outside the barrack.

He goes past the bread portions and is shaking with hunger. He must walk past quickly, otherwise he would bite into one of those pieces. Why is there no one there to watch over it? The bread is just there for the taking.

He does not walk past quickly. He lingers at the table and sniffs the aroma of the bread. No one is watching over him. And before he knows what he is doing, it happens: he seizes a portion of bread and puts it in his coat pocket. Then he walks slowly out of the barrack.

He is shaking even more than before; he sees flames before his eyes, and his teeth are chattering. He walks quickly now to get to his own barrack.

If they notice...

They will not notice. They will think that they have mistakenly left out one of the one hundred sixty or one hundred eighty portions; they will then cut off small pieces from the other portions and make a new portion from these pieces.

But if they notice...

He knows that he would then spend a couple of days in the bunker, in the cold and the dark, and they would withhold a portion of bread from him. That would be the only bad thing. And mother would cry, of course—that would be bad, too.

He climbs onto his bed. Mother is not there; she has work to do in a men's barrack. He takes the piece of bread out of his pocket and bites into it. Oh, how hungry he is! He hardly chews; he only swallows and swallows, big, hard pieces.

When most of the bread is gone, he stops eating. His throat hurts from swallowing, but he is no longer shaking. He buries his face in his straw pillow and curses. "Idiots!" he rages. "Idiots! Not to watch over your bread!"

Bath

AMID FIGHTING THE snowstorm and while holding her little sister's hand stiffly in her own, she is thinking:

"Formerly, at home, I heard the water running into the bathtub until it was full, and then I longed to go into the bathroom and lie in the water. The bathroom was warm from the hot water. As I lay in it, I let the soap make suds, until my hands were white. It smelled so good. The last year I bathed all alone, but mother laid out for me the big, rough bath towel and clean clothes. Usually I bathed before I got into bed; then my pyjamas lay ready for me, and it was so wonderful to get into bed, all clean and warm. And when my little sister was bathed, little rubber animals swam all around the tub, and she hit the water and splashed it everywhere, and then she squealed with pleasure. But I didn't know at the time how wonderful it was. In the future, when I have a bath again, I will appreciate how wonderful it is."

"Close in!" a voice calls behind her. An opening has come between her row of five and the row in front of her. The snowstorm is so dense and black that she can hardly see the backs of the five people in front of her. Everything is black—the air, the flakes, the ground. Formerly snow was always white; here, on the roll call field or between the barracks, there are moments when it is white and shining, too. But on this trip from the camp to the bathhouse—a building that is actually called the delousing center in Russian and German—on this trip everything is black. The flakes are swarming in front of her like black beasts. She can hardly keep her eyes open, and when her little sister complains that her face is hurting, she tells her to close her eyes because she will hold onto her. She is becoming terribly tired from it all—under the one arm both their bath towels, on her other hand her little sister who cannot go on, in front of her the storm and behind her the following row calling out, "Close in!"

How she will have to hurry later, now that she will have to wash her little sister and herself in those few minutes! Mother is at work in the shoe tent. The workers go to the bathhouse in their own groups. When mother was still able to go with them, she had enough trouble washing herself. She will let her little sister play with the soap a bit. The shower will rinse it off, at least if she can get a place under a shower. The other people always push so terribly after they have arrived at the bathhouse, and they undress much more quickly, thus they are also the first to get to the shower area. If there are already five women standing under one shower and you come join them, you get almost no water, except what drips off of the women— and that is so dirty...

Look, they are there now. Fortunately the wall of the bathhouse stands between them and the snowstorm. She can see again and catch her breath a bit before the door opens. Others are already flocking in front of the door, in order to be the first to go in. She cannot do that, certainly not with the little girl in hand. Perhaps she will be the last one again, and then the man in green will shout at her to hurry up. She cannot do anything about it.

Inside there is for each person a clothes hook on which you must hang all your clothes. You set your shoes on the floor, which is completely muddy from the melted snow from all those shoes. To walk on that muddy floor with your bare feet is a horrible feeling. Later, when your feet have been washed clean, they will immediately become dirty again, and then you will pull your stockings on over those dirty feet. Oh, well, those stockings are wet, anyway...

The people who were first to come inside have taken the clothes hooks that are farthest from the door. There is even a corner from which the heating comes; the ones who can undress there certainly are lucky! She is right by the outside door, and she and her little sister are shivering from the cold. When they are undressed, they put their towels around their shoulders. She pulls the corners forward, for she is a bit ashamed because her breasts are beginning to develop. It is very strange: you are proud that you are growing up, and you are ashamed at the same time.

The few hundred women wait naked in the following area. Again and again a group of about sixty is let into the shower room. The man in green who is standing by the entrance of the showers counts them, and when enough have gone inside, he shouts, "Halt!" to those following. After a few minutes the women who have showered come out, still wet because they have not had time to dry themselves. While drying themselves, they push alongside the wall of the crowded waiting area, back to their clothes.

Her turn will not come for a long time; there are two more groups in front of her. She cannot help that she sees a little bit around her. Her friend is standing a few rows ahead of her. How big she is! She does not look nearly as much like a grown-up when she has a dress on. The girl is nodding to her now; she hardly dares to nod back because all she has on is a towel over her shoulders.

There are a few elderly women in the group. In the barrack she saw that those old ones had preferred not to go through the snow, but the man in green who had to herd them all to the bathhouse called out something about lazy and filthy and that not *one* woman could remain behind in the barrack. Now those elderly women are standing here, shivering in the drafty waiting area. They look so horrible without their clothes on. She never knew that you became like that when you were old. She never wants to be old; she wants to remain just as she is now, or at the very oldest, to be mother's age, but she does not want to be old. Perhaps she will die before she gets to be so old, she thinks contentedly.

Watch out, now: she must go in with this group. She passes right by the man in green, who is counting throughout. Quickly—quickly—set the towels in a corner on the ground because there is nowhere to hang them—shove a little piece of soap into her sister's hand—see to it that they get under a shower...

She is quite fortunate; she goes under a shower where there were only three women. She and her sister make five. Bending, she shows the little girl what to do, and then she stretches her arms up toward the hot water. The water is actually clean, for it has not come dripping off from another woman first. Heavenly.

She lets the piece of soap glide along her body briefly, for she has no time to really wash herself. Oh, how *terribly* old that woman is next to her! Quickly she turns away. Has her little sister seen that, and was she also so shocked by it? She looks down where the little girl is squatting under the water, which is dripping down from the others.

Her little sister is absorbed in soaping the feet of the old woman. She is preoccupied with that and is thoroughly content.

She is not looking any higher than the ankles. Thank goodness.

Free Afternoon

WHEN FATHER HAS Sunday afternoon free—and that certainly does not happen all the time—then it is like a celebration. Beginning three days before, mother has been saving a potato from each of their rations. She has asked for the potato peels that the other women have thrown away, and she has patiently picked out all the scraps of potato. Fortunately she has time to do it; she does not have to go to work because the little one is not yet three years old. She has mashed all those potatoes and scraps with a fork. She has not eaten up her week's rations of jam or cheese, and now she mixes them with the potatoes, and if she can get a place at the stove on Sunday morning she makes a cake. She does not always get a place because there are so many who want one, and mother cannot shout as loudly as the other women, thus her turn does not come very quickly.

In the mornings there are always cauldrons full of hot, coffeelike liquid, without milk and sugar of course, but it makes swallowing your dry bread easier. There is more than enough of it; most women use it for washing dishes because it is hot, or for getting spots out of dark dresses. There is no hot water, thus that coffee comes in handy. But on Sunday morning mother takes her thermos bottle that she has taken from home, then to the previous camp, and then to this camp, and she fills it with coffee. When father has the afternoon free, and if mother has been able to use the stove to make a potato cake with dabs of jam on top, then they each get some coffee with a dash of her sister's milk, which the little girl receives because she is not yet three years old. They sit at their corner of the long table, then, each with a piece of potato cake and a mug of coffee with milk, and it is almost as festive and cozy as it used to be at home.

When father is *very* well rested—mother always says

that he might be tired and that they must leave him alone, but usually father just laughs at her—then they crawl into his lap and ask for stories. He used to be a school teacher, but now he must pull manure carts and dig trenches. Still, school teachers never forget that they have been school teachers and that they have told stories. A story that they do not yet know always appears from somewhere. It does not matter if they do know the story, but then father must be very careful that he does not make any mistakes, for otherwise they will tell it to him the correct way.

So, in father's lap, with a story and a piece of potato cake and a mug of coffee with milk, the barrack no longer exists at all, and the noise of other people and the crying of other children do not exist, either. There exists only a table, just like at home, and walls, just like in a room at home, and father and mother, just like at home. Sitting in father's lap, you stick your thumb in your mouth like a little child and think that everything is as it used to be.

Every Sunday morning at the end of work time they stand in front of the gate. If they see the people from the shoe tent coming back promptly, they are somewhat hopeful that the men from outdoor work, which includes father's group, will also return on time. But they often remain at work hours longer on Sunday; the men in green are angry about something, then, but no one knows why—and so there is punishment. Late in the afternoon the workers come back to their barrack, tired and hungry, and when father has eaten, there really can be no story remaining for her, and no lap, either.

When the weather is nice, they take a walk on the small or large roll call field; she walks at father's and mother's hand while her sister rides in the little folding cart. Sometimes they sit in the sun, at the edge of a barrack. But if they are unable to do this on a Sunday, it is usually because the men have received another sort of punishment. The workers return at the normal time, but as they are eating, the message goes around that they must report to the midday call, just as they do during the week. They must finish their meal quickly, otherwise they will be late. They usually do not go back to work, then, but have punishment drills: for hours at a time they must walk and stand and kneel and walk quickly with their knees bent, and when they are tired, they do not do it well enough, and then they must drill even longer in order to learn it better. If a few come late to midday call, those people receive extra punishment, but then everyone must remain there longer. Therefore all the workers look very angrily at the latecomers because they have brought punishment upon them all. And of course when all those long hours are past, there is no time left for pleasure. Father usually goes to his own barrack to lie down. Together with mother they bring him his piece of cake and mug of coffee, and he thanks them very nicely, but he cannot even smile at them anymore.

How really strange it is, that you can be punished when you have not done anything! Father and mother are not like that; they almost never punish you, but if they do, then you have done something *very* naughty!

But it happens here because the men in green are always angry at you. They do not like Jews. Whenever they see your star they are reminded that you are Jewish. And there are so *many* stars and so *many* Jews here. That makes them angry, and then they punish you. But you cannot help it that you are Jewish, can you? And that you wear a star? You have to.

It is such a shame. And it is also very difficult to understand. Later, perhaps...

Neighbor Below

OF ALL THE nasty and unpleasant old people there are, he is certain that the woman below him is the nastiest and most unpleasant of them all. Of course, it is true that never before in his life has he lived *so* close to an old person; when you sleep above someone, the two of you have a lot of contact with each other.

Because she lies in bed the whole day, she is bothered when he climbs up to his bed and when he climbs down. It cannot be helped that he must put his foot on the edge of her bed, for otherwise he cannot climb up and down. And she also complains that straw falls on her when he is up on his bed. He hasn't made the straw mattress, has he? As if he does it on purpose!

She coughs at night. Oh, yes, a lot of people cough— but you still do not have to make such a production of it! She pants and makes all sorts of noises that you normally do not make when you cough, thus he knows for sure that she is putting on airs. Mother does not hear any of it, for she sleeps in a different passageway, and if you are not right above someone, then you do not hear so much. Not that he sleeps badly—not at all! He doesn't put on any airs! But during the moments when he is awake, he hears her coughing and panting and doing strange things, and then he becomes irritable from anger and impatience.

It has never been as it is tonight. He really cannot go back to sleep now. Why don't they give her cough medicine in the evening, such as he used to get at home when he had a cough? Why don't they do something about it?

Someone else has heard it now. Someone with a lantern is coming to the old woman's bed. He hears how someone is saying a few soothing words to her. It is the voice of the barrack nurse, but the old woman does not answer. She only pants in a very strange, rattling manner.

The nurse does not say anything more to her because she is not getting any answer. She goes away with her lamp, and he is afraid that she will not do anything for her, but shortly after the nurse returns with another woman. It is a barrack leader. They whisper a bit together; he cannot hear what they are saying.

Luckily the panting has become somewhat less. Perhaps they have done something for her, after all. She remains quiet for a long time between the one pant and the next, so that each time he thinks that it is over; then suddenly it comes again.

Now those two women are doing something very strange: together they are partly whispering and partly saying aloud "Shema," and then other Jewish prayers. When they stop, he hears the nurse say, "It's over."

Suddenly he understands. She was not pretending and she could not help it at all and it was very cruel of him to be so angry with her and he will never again, *never* again be angry with someone who coughs and pants. For his neighbor below is dead.

"What shall we do?" whispers the nurse.

He is lying with his head at the edge of his bed in order to hear what they are saying. He hopes that the nurse will continue watching over her, for they must not leave him alone above that old dead woman. They can't do that!

"Don't do anything," says the barrack leader. "Don't make a commotion. Cover her up until early in the morning when it's light."

He wants to say that they must not leave him alone, but he is ashamed that he has heard it all. It is as if he has been eavesdropping and has heard something that was not intended for children. He sees the little light going away, and he knows that he is alone above his dead neighbor.

Now that she is dead, perhaps she knows everything— even all his ugly thoughts about her and how furious he was with her tonight. He tries to think nice things about her, but then he remembers her old, grumbling voice that complained about his feet on the edge of her bed and about the straw, and then all his nice thoughts cease. How awful that is! You cannot help what you think about someone, and now she knows everything and she thinks that he is an even nastier boy than before!

The worst thing is that because of all the shock and all the lying in bed while awake, he has to go to the bathroom. In the pitch-black he will have to step on the edge of her bed, and she is dead. If he were bigger, he would let himself down with his hands from the edge of his own bed and just drop down; but he is too small, and he would certainly break his legs doing that. He will have to step on her bed.

In the moment when he is standing on her bed with his bare feet, he has the feeling that he is touching her. Immediately he jumps to the floor, scrambles under the bed for his shoes, and runs away, bumping into everything in the narrow passageway.

When he returns from the bathroom, he knows that he cannot step on her bed again or go back to his own bed. He feels his way to another passageway and gropes along the beds and counts them, to find mother's bed.

"What is it?" asks mother, startled from her sleep when his head and his arms come up above the edge of her bed. "Is there something the matter?"

"I'm afraid—mother, I'm afraid—oh, mother, may I come into your bed just this once?" he whispers nervously. Mother has already pulled him up over the edge and is holding the blanket up so that he can crawl under it.

"Did you have a bad dream?" she asks.

Did he dream it? Oh, no—it really happened. He shivers.

"There, there," says mother and lays his head against her cheek. "Is it good now?"

"Yes," he says wearily.

Mother does not half know *how* good it is.

They Put Their Heads Together

TODAY THERE CAN be no club or lessons or school or whatever you want to call it; there has been an extra roll call because there were not enough workers, thus child care was immediately forbidden, and the teacher was sent to the shoe tent to tear apart old shoes. They will have to be on their own today.

Fortunately it is dry weather, otherwise they would have to hang about the barrack and receive scoldings from screaming mothers because they are sitting everywhere when there is nothing to sit on. They saunter outside from the different barracks and find each other and do not yet know what they are going to do.

The French children are lucky. They have kept their young teacher and are playing a game in a ring and are singing a French song that the others do not understand but that they enjoy listening to because it sounds so funny. The Greek children have *never* done anything. They always do exactly what they want, just like the adult Greeks. The Jewish overseer of the camp—the man who blows the whistle when roll call is over—is Greek himself, and he may do whatever he wishes. The little Italians from North Africa have hardly anything to do with the camp. They have a teacher with a stick, and if there is a Hebrew word they do not know, they receive a rap of that stick on the leg. They are always walking on the roll call field and having lessons in a circle, and the men in green seem to approve because they cannot understand each other, anyway. You can understand only the few boys who know a mouthful of Hebrew—if you yourself know Hebrew, that is! In any case, these little brown children are not troubled that child care is forbidden; they receive it just as well from the stick.

But the ordinary children who speak Dutch or a Germanic Dutch—there are no real English children, although there are a lot who have some English papers even though they do not know a word of English—the ordinary children do not know how to begin their day. There is no air raid alarm, thus they can walk freely between the barracks; but you reach the end of your walk, and then what? Together you can look for wood chips for the stove in the mess hall; when there are no more chips to be found, then you are no further than you were before.

A group of boys is hanging about near the barbed wire. They are looking out onto the broad space between the camp and the kitchen, an area along which the workers always walk to work. One of the boys there can always tell beforehand what the food will be the next day, for his father sleeps next to one of the cooks. Not that it always comes out right—sometimes he hears it incorrectly, and sometimes he tells it as he would like it to be.

"Tomorrow evening we are having thick soup," he says triumphantly, looking at the kitchen on the other side.

"No we aren't!" a few call out. "We have thick soup only two times a week, and we've already had it two times this week!"

"Oh, no? The cook said so. From now on we get it three times a week."

"You'll see!" they jeer.

"And I know more. Tonight we're having sweet coffee."

"Really?"

Why is it that they do not jeer at the sweet coffee? Sweet coffee is even more scarce than thick soup; they have had it only two or three times. Perhaps they cannot imagine that a boy would make up such a thing as sweet coffee.

"Really. Watch for it tonight."

A small group of political prisoners comes by on its way to work. Their legs can hardly support them as they drag themselves forth in their striped prison uniforms with a cross or numbers or a death's head painted in red. On their heads, which have been shaved bald, they wear striped cotton caps, which they must quickly remove for each man in green who comes by.

"Those are streeflingen,"* says a boy. "Because of those stripes on their clothes, of course."

---

* The boy is referring to "Sträflinge," the German word for "convicts."—Translators

---

224

"Oh, come on! Streeflingen is German! Because they are being punished!"

"Then they should be called sträflingen, shouldn't they?"

They look at the staggering little group and are glad that their fathers wear their own, ordinary clothes, even if they do drag heavy carts and work as though they were streeflingen. The boys discuss the contents of each cart that is pulled past them; perhaps there is something other than turnips in that cart which is parked in front of the kitchen. They cannot see it from here.

"No—turnips," declares the son of the neighbor of the cook. He speaks firmly and in a businesslike way. No one listens to him.

Then a manure cart drawn by a horse rides by. A Sträfling is in the driver's seat, and in the wagon, in a stack, are long, filled burlap sacks. The man in the driver's seat, who is not allowed to talk to anyone from the Jewish camp, puts five fingers up to a Jew passing by.

The Jew nods and sadly shakes his head.

"Do you know what those are, in that wagon?" calls a boy excitedly. "Those are dead people!"

"You're crazy!"

"No—I know it! Five dead people from the barrack of the streeflingen! He showed with his hand that there were five! I saw it myself!"

"Five from *one* barrack—that can't be, can it? And in sacks?"

"Yes," says the boy proudly. "That's what happens to the streeflingen. Why—sometimes even a lot more than five!"

The others are silent, impressed by so much knowledge. It could be—yes, of course, it *could* be true. They are being punished, and everything is very different, then. What have they done to receive punishment? Something very bad, perhaps...

Silently they stand watching the cart until it passes by the next barbed wire fence.

Old Tales

ON THE EVENING of Purim a couple of men hurry after work to the barracks of their wives and children. They have the small roll of parchment with them that they have brought from home. The story of Purim is in it—the old story of Jews in need and of an unexpected rescue, of a young, brave queen who dedicated herself to her people, of chances that turned about in just one day. The women and children must hear that story now more than in any other year. The men in the men's camp can hear it this evening; the men with the parchment will not be chased out of there in half an hour, as they will be here.

A man sets himself at one of the tables and rolls out the parchment under the circle of light given off by the weak lamp on the ceiling. He begins to read, hurriedly yet with emphasis on every word of that strange story that is not stranger or anymore moving than his own life has been in the last years. A circle forms around him; in front are the children, behind them, the mothers. For some of them this Hebrew is as open and as absorbing as a story told in their mother tongue. For some the Hebrew words are the faithful sounds from their youth, thus merely sweet and pleasing. For some it is new and from a distant world. The circle grows with each minute. Those in the very back do not see the man, and they hear his voice only remotely. No one wants to miss this recitative spoken in monotone. Isn't it a story that really happened, and can't it happen again tomorrow? Can't the rescue come from a side that you have not seen and for which you dare not to hope?

When the story is over, the man runs away through the nearly closed barbed wire gate that separates the women's camp from the men's. Such a thing you must not do—to tell children and mothers a story that revives their hope. But you do it, nonetheless, and you run back blissfully content to tell the story once more to your barrack mates.

The next afternoon the children have a party. No man in green must notice it, and there is constantly a woman on the lookout; if the men in green should know that it was a festive day, they would keep the workers longer and give them extra-heavy work to do. It is the secret of each barrack that has children—the glowing secret. The mothers have given all the children a potato and a lick of jam, and a few of the handiest have kept the stove burning until yesterday evening when the light went out and have made a festive cake. A few mothers have found tablecloths in their suitcases. All the children have on the prettiest clothes that could appear from their rucksacks. Their hair is wet from combing and from trying to curl it in the bathroom. There are a few children with colorful clothes on, for you must dress up on Purim, and why can't you be Queen Esther, even in a barrack?

Oh, what a celebration it is! There is a man who can sing, and they have secretly kept him away from the shoe tent and have sent a volunteer in his place, in order to send the full quota of workers. He goes from the one barrack where there are children, to another, the whole afternoon. He sings, and he has the children sing, and he receives pieces of potato cake and mugs of black liquid that is supposed to be coffee, and he becomes merry and drunk from it. On Purim you must become *so* drunk that you no longer curse your enemy. He is drunk from the coffee, and he no longer curses anyone; he blesses, he blesses these children and these mothers and the young, brave queen who dedicated her life to her people. He is *so* drunk that he no longer sees a difference between the need of the present and the rescue in the past. Oh—but it is such an old story...

And when it is Passover...

Did it happen today? Yesterday? Did the children of Israel have to pull manure carts and dig trenches and tear apart old shoes in Egypt? No: they had to bake bricks and build cities and pyramids. Was that Pharaoh in Egypt who furiously roared, "Lazy—what lazy people you are!"? No: it was the men in green uniform with a death's head as insignia and symbol. Was it the overseers in Egypt who were threatened with punishment when the enslaved masses did not turn out more work? No: it was the barrack leaders. Was it the bread of affliction that would not rise? No: it was the dry, hard pieces of dark bread, measured in centimeters and greedily devoured without butter. Was that the night of deliverance, when...

Oh, no—don't think about it anymore. It is so confusing.

But when it is the evening of the Seder, the beginning of Passover—the evening when everywhere in the world the youngest Jew present asks why this night is different from all other nights, then the men hurry again to the barracks of their wives and children. The symbols that must bring to life the answer to the question of the youngest have already been made ready by women's hands. But the symbols are different from those on all other Seder evenings.

There is no matzo on the Seder platter to remember both the bread of affliction and the haste in which the children of Israel left Egypt, the haste that did not allow them the time for their bread to rise. Their own bread is bread of affliction enough. There is no bitter herb on the Seder platter to remember the bitterness of slavery; the daily turnips are reminder enough of the bitterness of their own slavery. There is no bone and no egg on the Seder platter to remember the Passover sacrifice, which each Israelite accounted for to be among those who were prepared for deliverance. Each person is prepared for deliverance— but there *is* nothing so poor here; there is only an unpeeled potato instead of the egg, and a little piece of meat, fished out from the turnips.

"Why is this night different from all other nights?"

A little girl asks, and the man answers. He answers with the old tale of oppression and deliverance. The faces in the circle around him are gentle and happy; they know oppression, and they believe in deliverance.

For star children do not *learn* history—they *live* history. And if they did not believe in deliverance, their history would have been over long ago: an old story with an unhappy ending.

The story is not over—not for a *long* time!

The Chosen

INCOMPREHENSIBLE—OH, INCOMPREHENSIBLE!

At the moment when the workers had their afternoon roll call and were to have gone their usual way—out the gate, each group to its own place of work—the commanding voice of a man in green called, "People with Palestine papers will not go to work! Remain in your roll call place!"

Not go to work. A command not to go to work. To see the other groups leaving, the dreary, trudging line of twice a day, and to remain behind because you have papers for Palestine.

Children who have seen and heard it run back to the barracks to shout it all around. No one believes it; so often hope flames up and is quickly extinguished again. Who is there who can still expect something good from this star hell? Those who enter it leave all hope behind.

From far away the children listen, who, disappointed, have had no faith, and the few mothers, who have let themselves be taken in; they listen to what is being said to the workers who have remained behind on the roll call field. A few cunning people have gone into the barrack that looks out on the roll call field. No one pays attention to them or sends them out.

"Back to your barracks, and within ten minutes be here with all your papers and all your family!"

Incomprehensible—oh, incomprehensible!

During the six days of creation, the universe waited for the beginning of each new day no less breathlessly than it waited for God's new word of creation here in the camp.

The roll call field is the universe for those who are standing here and listening to the chosen names, and with each new name a world is created or destroyed. A world opens for the one who hears his name called. For the one who hears his letter in the alphabet go by without hearing the sound of his own name, the world perishes.

The chosen stand in a separate group, in rows of five. What is going to happen to them? Something good, of course. Perhaps they will go to a better camp, more to the south, to the east, closer to Palestine. Perhaps to a free country. That they will go to Palestine itself—no one thinks about that except the children. Of course, you have to be a child to believe in fairy tales—and here on the roll call field, where there has been *so* much suffering, and always with the barking voice of a man in green above your heads, Palestine *is* a fairy tale, isn't it? Lucky children...

When the list is finished, no one understands which group is the chosen one. Those whose lives are the most closely tied to Palestine have been left out, and those who barely wish to ever see it have been chosen. The two groups stand opposite each other and look at each other in silence; a few children in the omitted group begin to cry. The whistle blows just as it does every day when roll call is over. The two groups, which have suddenly become one, return to their barracks. Mothers comfort crying children, and wives comfort bewildered husbands.

"It will amount to nothing again," say the grown-ups.

But the children who have heard their names called take their belongings out of their rucksacks and pack them in again. *They* are ready for the journey to Palestine.

The next morning the people with papers for Palestine go to work as usual. But in the afternoon they must remain behind, just like yesterday—all of them.

A few names have been taken off yesterday's list, and a few names have been added on. Is this a game of the devil that is being played with them? How much of this tension can they go through, without going crazy and bringing death and destruction over the camp?

They stand in two groups again. But now the group of those left behind is chased back to the barrack with a snarl, and the group of the chosen is spoken to in a tone that is new to this camp: as if the words were being directed to people. Within half an hour they must return to the roll call field with all their baggage.

Are they going on a journey, today already? Where will they go? And do the men in green actually believe that those in the group will forget all the indignity and humiliation at one blow, if at the last moment they are spoken to as if they were human beings?

Slowly they shuffle forward in rows of five. They go out the one camp gate, as if they were going to the bathhouse—and they go into the next gate, to a brick barrack that is no longer part of this camp and that is separated from it by barbed wire.

This is the journey: from the one camp to the one next to it. But the journey is also to another world, where there is no slave labor, where roll call takes at most fifteen minutes, and where the men in green speak instead of shout.

The barrack has the shape of a stable. Each person looks for a bed and settles himself in again, as if no one had ever thought about a journey.

"Do you have to lead the barrack again?" asks the little girl, disheartened, whose mother was a barrack leader.

"No," says the mother, blissfully happy. "I don't have to be *anything* here."

"*Just* a mother!" cheers the little girl.

That evening they see through the barbed wire the adults and children of the old camp standing at roll call for hours and hours, until darkness falls.

French

IT IS MARVELOUS—the grown-ups teach you so much
when they do not have anything else on their hands! In
the other camp most of the fathers and mothers were at
work the whole day, and gradually most of the teachers
went to work, too; but here they have all the time in the
world, and they can teach you as much as they want.

Not that she doesn't like it—learning doesn't make
any difference to her; it is neither pleasant nor unpleasant.
It was the same way at school, too. She saw to it that she
was promoted to the next grade every year, which was not
much trouble for her, but she never did receive high
marks.

Oh, well—if you can give the grown-ups some pleasure...

She counted on doing a lot of playing and a lot of
running on the small roll call field now that everything in
this new barrack is so different from the previous one. But
there is also time left over for other activities, and the
grown-ups themselves are learning just as rapidly as the
children, or even more rapidly. Hebrew—always and
everywhere is Hebrew. They are still hoping that they will
be sent to Palestine, and if you do not know any Hebrew,
then there you stand with a mouthful of teeth. There are
grown-ups who must still learn to read Hebrew, and there
are grown-ups who at the Hebrew lesson speak to each
other as if it were nothing and who can retell those whole
books in Hebrew. There is an old man and woman who are
afraid that they will not have learned their lesson for their
teacher, and in the evening they always walk arm-in-arm,
back and forth over the roll call field, and listen to each
other's words.

She herself has learned to read Hebrew, and she also
knows a few words, and she knows how very differently
Hebrew fits together than Dutch does, but that is it. The
funny thing is, everything that she learned in all her sub-

jects at school is coming up again now that she has been set to work at her studies once more. You get a bit of pleasure from that. But she would never do what the adults do. In the evenings the grown-ups go listen to a speaker in the men's barrack; they may do that because in this camp they are never chased away from each other in the evening and because there is never inspection in the evening. But she would not go to hear a speaker for any amount of money. She yawns when she even thinks about it. Of course, the grown-ups are so happy that they can now do what they want—and *if* they want to go listen to a speaker...

Just at the moment when she wants to go out of the latrine, which is much nicer here than on the other side of the barbed wire, she sees that on the white plastered wall a whole history has been written in pencil. She goes to it to see what it is, and laughs out loud in surprise; it is French!

It begins with "Nous sommes," and that sounds just like a sentence from an exercise, for at school she had just had "j'ai—tu as—il a—nous avons—vous avez—ils ont" and also "je suis—tu es—il est—nous sommes—vous êtes—ils sont," thus "nous sommes" is familiar enough. Thank goodness she had learned her French lesson then and that she remembers everything, otherwise the writing would have meant nothing to her.

"Nous sommes les juifs de Warschawa."

Juifs is Jews, but she cannot make anything else out. She will go fetch mother—perhaps she will understand it all, and she is so intent on learning right now...

While she is passing by she sees one more sentence written elsewhere, apart from the rest:

"Nous partirons pour l'exchange."

Partir is leave—she still knows that from the lesson about the train. Pour is for. Of course, mother will know it.

She is a bit excited by this peculiar writing, as she brings mother to the latrine. She proudly shows her that it actually is French, that little lesson on the wall there.

"Perhaps it is a military secret!" she says to mother. "And I have discovered it!"

Mother reads it silently to herself. What she reads is this:

"Nous sommes des juifs de Warschawa. Tout le ghetto de Warschawa a été brulé. Tout les juifs du ghetto ont été tués par le gaz ou le ———. Ils se sont défendus comme des héros. Hommage à eux, qui sont nos frères, nos héros. Nous espérons partir pour l'exchange, pour Palestine."*

"Yes," says mother aloud.

"What is it?" she asks tensely. The success is not as great as she had hoped.

"Oh...nothing...says mother dreamily. "A bit of history."

"French history?"

"No," mother slowly shakes her head. "No—Jewish."

Game of Dice

SHAVUOT—OH, A shining, glorious day!

The children take out their prettiest and thinnest dresses and strut back and forth over the roll call field. Before roll call begins on the other side of the barbed wire, the adults and children pretend to walk a bit near the barbed wire, but in the meanwhile they call out greetings to each other and wish each other a happy holiday. They

---

*We are Jews of Warsaw. The entire Warsaw ghetto has been burned. All the Jews of the ghetto have been killed by gas or by [an illegible word]. They defended themselves as heroes. Honor them, our brothers, our heroes. We hope to leave for Palestine, for exchange.

know how dangerous it is; the two camps must not come into contact with each other or speak to each other, and if the man in the watchtower notices it, he will shoot without warning, but how can you help calling out good things to each other on such a sunny day, and a holiday, besides?

Soon, when the men in green are in the lucky camp for the short, easy roll call—what is it to count three hundred Jews!—then they particularly must not notice that it is a holiday, for otherwise those in the other camp would have to work twice as hard and would have to stand at roll call for hours longer. The children's festive little dresses can do no harm; the shining day can be the reason for that.

There is surprise in the air. There must, there *must* be something good that will happen today...

It is afternoon and a bit hot to be thinking about surprises. The American airplanes go high above the camp like a swarm of white, glittering birds, and the air raid alarm makes the roads between the barracks appear deserted. Suddenly the air raid alarm is stopped for this Palestine camp; everyone must appear immediately at the small roll call area. What for? It must be for something good! Today it cannot be anything else but for something good! The children scream and cheer with expectation, but the grown-ups, afraid that whatever it is that is good will be taken away from them again if the children do not behave themselves, are strict and urge them to be quiet.

Yes, it is something good. The commandant is there and another man in green, a very powerful one who comes to the camp only when there is something going on with exchanging prisoners. It will actually come to a journey now; where they will go does not matter!

Trained by the daily experience of half a year, they quickly line up in rows of five, the children in front of the adults. The calling out of names and birthdates begins. Those whose names are called must go stand apart, again in rows of five. It seems like what happened on the big roll call field on the other side of the barbed wire five weeks ago; but then there stood more than one thousand, and now there are only three hundred waiting for their

235

names. A few names have dropped out of this alphabetical series. Those who have been omitted look at each other; what does this mean? Perhaps there will be a replacement later, when the alphabet is finished. They are uneasy, however.

The commandant, who is not reading the names himself, jumps up again and again and peers uneasily through his binoculars at the glittering specks in the air. He has called off the air raid alarm for these couple of barracks because this has to be done quickly, but he himself is in the open air, too, and you never know what those airplanes are going to do.

The star children and their fathers and mothers have other things to think about than airplanes. A bomb or a shooting while nose diving—who cares? If you are redeemed or not—if your name is omitted or not...

"Inside!" orders the commandant. "Later go stand in the same formation again!"

Middle in the alphabet. And no one knows if those omitted will still be named at the end or who from the remainder of the alphabet will drop out.

There is a little star girl who has come here on the certificate of another woman. That woman was able to keep the child from going to Poland because she adopted her in order to return her to her own parents in Palestine; they had to leave her behind five years ago, when she was a baby. Perhaps the parents no longer know that their daughter is still alive. The name of the little star girl is called—but the foster mother is omitted. What does it mean? There is a father and a mother whose oldest girl is *so* sick that only a very speedy departure from this star hell can save her. There, in Palestine—once she is there... but they are omitted. What does it mean? The adults ask it of each other, but the children who have been omitted are quiet. And those who are not quiet are threatened with a snarl to be quiet by mothers who otherwise never snarl and threaten. Oh, God, why don't they know anything, and why has it been broken off midway through!

Then the all-clear signal sounds, and defeated by tension they return to their places.

The list continues. More names are dropped, and when the alphabet is finished, there stands on the one side the group of those called up and on the other side a small group of fifty who have been forgotten. There are no replacements; the tension is over. In a businesslike manner the commandant informs the ones called up that they will probably travel this week. The number was too large, and in Berlin fifty names were struck from the list. There is nothing he can do. Whoever has a question can ask it.

A few come forward, even though they know that nothing is going to be changed. The little star girl, her hand in her foster mother's, stands there, too.

"Commandant," sings her high little voice. "Say, commandant, do I have to go to Palestine *alone?* Commandant, *listen now! Do I have to go to Palestine alone?*"

Cornered, the commandant is silent. The little star girl shrugs her shoulders.

"He doesn't understand me," she says, disappointed.

The foster mother lifts up the child and offers her for sale.

"Which woman wants to watch over this child on the journey?" she asks.

A few women raise their hands. The foster mother hesitates a little, looks along the hands and faces, and chooses. She says nothing; she kisses the child and passes her over to the new foster mother. A dream vanishes; a dream of insanely happy parents who get a living child back from her hands. They will get her back—but the dream, *her* dream, the realization of which would have been worth an entire life, the dream has vanished.

The child stands beaming in the row of those called up and nods triumphantly to the woman who has returned to the row of those who have been omitted.

"I get to go to Palestine!" resounds her little voice.

The fifty who are being sent back must pack their rucksacks and return to the other side of the barbed wire.

Quickly—quickly—for suddenly they are no longer human beings to whom one speaks in a decent tone of voice but numbers from the slave camp, which must be chased and shouted at. Quickly—quickly—do not mix the two kinds together—and hurry up!

The lucky ones who will travel this week do what they can to help. Their joy is melting into the suffering of the others. Oh, this game of dice—this playing high with people's lives!

On the other side of the barbed wire the fifty drag their loads forth with difficulty and wait to be divided among the barracks. Everything is just as it was five weeks ago; tomorrow they will be sent to work again or stand for hours at roll call.

A little star boy, his thin, white face so distorted that it appears masklike, turns and peers over the roll call field at the barbed wire and what lies in back of it: five weeks of paradise.

The mother, who herself is crouched and defeated, lays a comforting hand on his shoulder. But the boy pulls his shoulder away from under her hand and growls hoarsely, "Leave me alone."

Then, frightened by the dismay shown in her face, he turns around and cries as a boy cries: raw and wild, and without tears.

Back and Forth

WHEN SHE LOOKS back at what has happened in those few weeks, after those fifty people were sent away since they could not make the journey...

She has done everything with her friend, for she herself has no family here. Father and mother have long been in Palestine, ever since half a year after they had sent her to Holland, to safety. They sent her to Holland because there had been such a terrible night in Germany and because they did not want their little girl—she was ten at the time—to be there if it happened again. Oh, later on in Holland there were many more nights and days that were just as awful—and worse for her than that one in Germany, because in Holland she was living with strangers and not with father and mother and because she was bigger and understood everything much better. If she had not been sent to Holland at that time, she would already have been in Palestine with father and mother for a long time now—but they could not have known that beforehand. And that she will now travel to father and mother, that she cannot yet believe—not even now.

On one morning in the week after Shavuot it is said that in a few hours they must have their baggage ready to be inspected and weighed. They actually believed then, that the trip would be on that day. The men in green believed it, too, otherwise they would not have gone to the trouble of the weighing. But in the afternoon when they were standing ready, tired and sweaty and very tense, suddenly the command came to go back to the barrack again and make up their beds, for the trip was being postponed indefinitely.

Everyone knew, then, what "indefinitely" meant: forever. They will never, never get away from here. It is even worse than it was for those fifty who were sent back, for they did not have their baggage ready and weighed. However, they do not have to return to the camp where they would immediately be put to work again. They remain together—a group of two hundred fifty who were bound for Palestine.

But a week and a half later there is suddenly a very different command: to move back to the old camp; not yet to work—not yet to be divided among the other barracks. They will be together in one small, stuffy barrack, which was quickly emptied for them and not even cleaned.

They are *still* together—but the men in green are shouting again just as they always did when you were in the old camp. Their tone of voice changed even before they began to move. They can drag their baggage themselves, and quickly, too! Yes, that old woman there, too—she is just pretending to be so old!

"How old are you?" shouts the man in green to the old woman, who is attempting to move her rucksack onward.

"Seventy-seven," she says in a strong voice.

"You're lying."

The old woman beams with pride because he does not believe that she actually is seventy-seven. It gives her such energy that she is able to drag the rucksack much farther.

And so they have come back to the old camp again, and the others who have not been away are so full of pity that they hardly dare to look at them.

But *she* takes pity on those others who have had to go along in their rut without stopping, without weeks of relief. She enjoyed each day in the other camp and because she never actually believed that she would go to her father and mother in Palestine she is not very disappointed at all. She was just as hungry there as she will be here, thus that does not make much difference. No—she has had it good, and what further comes she will take in stride.

What further comes...

A week later they are forced into work again. There must be such-and-such a number of workers supplied from their barrack; the leaders themselves must search them out. Because she had a birthday in the other camp and has turned fifteen, and because otherwise the mothers with little children would perhaps be sent, she reports to the barrack leaders. Her friend is not yet fifteen, otherwise they could go together. The parents of her friend do not like it at all that she will go to that dusty shoe tent, but she has already reported for work happily, and there is nothing more to be done about it now.

She is a bit excited when she goes for the first time. It is an adventure. But as she sits for hours, bent as a hoop because hunger has left her so little energy in her back and because she does not even know what the back of a chair looks like anymore, then the excitement disappears, and not much adventure remains, either. It is dirty and dusty, and the sun shines down on the tent with all those hundreds of people inside and makes it boiling hot. But the women at her table tell each other delicious recipes from the past; that helps ease the hunger. And the girl across from her listens to her Hebrew words that she learned in the other camp. Thus the time passes.

In the afternoon she sees that the woman next to her tears shoes only when the man in green comes near them to look and to bark a little. When he is not there, the woman makes from the snips of leather the nicest flowers and corsages that she can devise. When the girl discovers it, she becomes wide-awake with pleasure. She asks if she may copy it.

"If you are just as careful as I am," says the woman, and suddenly begins to tear shoes again because behind them a man in green is standing and watching. She is alarmed by it, for she had not seen him coming at all, but as soon as he is gone again, she follows the nimble fingers of her neighbor and copies her art. She is handy, and that afternoon she brings a brown corsage back with her for her friend's brown coat.

So, with watching out for the men in green, and Hebrew words and corsages, it is bearable. For a week or whatever, at least...

And now, very early in the morning, something has suddenly come up, something that she cannot completely comprehend and believe: the sudden command to quickly pack, for today the journey to Palestine will take place.

"It isn't true," she thinks all the while she is packing her belongings for the umpteenth time. "It isn't true that I'm going to father and mother. It hasn't been true all those other times."

But it *could* be true this time. They may not even say their farewells to the rest of the camp; there is someone standing watch to keep all the others away. But from a distance they wave and call to each other, and those who are leaving good friends weep from afar because perhaps they will never see one another again. It *could* be true, then, when the men in green are so strict and when they look over the luggage so carefully!

"It isn't true. Oh, let me believe that it isn't true!" But she is beginning to believe it.

At the end of that strange, busy morning, the men in green have almost finished examining the baggage, throwing away all papers and letters, and taking away all medicines. The chosen have made themselves ready to leave the camp. All their belongings are left behind in a heap, and they hold only a small bag in their hands. A few of those who had been sent back are now called out of the camp because perhaps they still may be allowed to go, too. A few of those chosen are very sick and would die if they began the journey, and there is an old mother who would rather remain with her children and grandchildren. Thus instead of these people who will not be going, those other few are called. They stand across from the commandant in silence and dismay, and wait to see what is so suddenly being decided about their fates. The foster mother of the little girl who is going to be brought back to her parents is there, too; she is very white because she is beginning to believe that her dream will be fulfilled now. After their papers have been examined, they must run back to their barrack to throw their belongings into a rucksack and go with the rest. It is high time.

The exodus begins: out the gate, as if they were going to the bathhouse. But this time they are not going to the bathhouse or to another barrack, either. They are going farther. Whereto? Whereto?

From everywhere the groups of Jews at work call out their good wishes. They call softly and without turning their faces toward them; they must not come into contact, these two kinds of Jews! But the good wishes still reach them and hurt them because they are leaving all those others behind.

She and her friend walk along either side of her friend's mother. They are tired from the moving events of the morning, and they cannot talk. Whatever they have to say would always come to the same thing: where are they going? And they still would not be able to answer that question. They must stop in front of a large garage. Trucks and a few small automobiles are driven out of it. They will surely spend the night there, until they actually depart, therefore the garage must be emptied first.

They stand waiting in the fierce sun and do not know how they can remain upright. They may not go sit on the ground.

An old woman who had not understood that she could have waited for a truck to bring the old and sick here asks the man in green if she may go inside the garage and look for a place to rest.

"Oh, well!" he calls. "My mother is eighty-two, and she sits in the air-raid shelter every night!"

She hears it because she has been walking right behind the old woman. Suddenly she has a strange feeling of pity for that man who roars and shouts so and who is so harsh, because his mother sits in the air-raid shelter every night. She is terribly ashamed that she has pity for a man in green who has no pity for a single one of them. She will never dare to tell it.

When they are finally able to go into the emptied garage, they go sit on the ground with as many people as possible against a wall. They become very dirty, but they could not stand up any longer. At least it is cool here.

They they must stand in a row for a long time to be looked over and felt by an old German woman to see if they have hidden anything in their clothes. Oh, they have nothing hidden, and they would not want to hide anything, either. They want so very much to get away from here without anything—why would they want to hide anything?

Night has come. The men have come and were examined. The elderly have come in a truck. Bread has been brought, and they have eaten, sitting in the dust in the garage and wiping their dirty hands on their clothes. There is talk about dividing into compartments, though they can hardly believe in compartments in which they will actually sit. A man in green read aloud rules for the trip, about not drinking too much alcohol and also something about a dining car, and then everyone laughed the way you laugh at a good joke. Much has happened and much has come to pass, but she is *so* tired that she hardly knows why she is here in a strange garage and not in the barrack that had grown so familiar to her. She is no longer thinking about Palestine at all. She and her friend sit with their backs leaning against each other, and they sleep, short sleeps that seem long whenever they awaken with a start.

When they have finally been shaken completely awake, they hear the command, that familiar command of each day:

"In rows of five!"

It takes a few minutes before she understands that she is not on the way to the shoe tent but to freedom.

Flap of Wings

IN THE DARK of the summer night they walk on the road that goes through the big camp. To the side they see the bathhouse rising up like a shadow. Until now the bathhouse has been the end of each trip, and when they went there, they would see a forest road glimmering in the distance that would evoke feelings of homesickness for rest and freedom. They know that they are now on their way to what always remained an enticing distance to them.

They do not go quickly. Some of them can hardly go forth after the day they experienced yesterday, which passed into the night of the present and which almost reaches into the day of tomorrow. The man in green who accompanies them does not hurry them along this time. There is no work to which they must be driven; there is only freedom in the distance.

They are both walking again on either side of her friend's mother. She feels herself quietly hidden away next to a mother in the night. The smell of the forest that was always far away is already coming closer. It is good to walk toward the smell of a forest and not to think about what will happen next.

The people in the front come to a halt. They wait until the slower ones have joined them. There must be something that is keeping them back, thus they must be closed in before they continue on their way.

And then, looking ahead, she sees what has been holding back those in the lead. Slowly, glittering-white in the moonlight, the barrier rises. That barrier marks the end of the camp; behind it lies the world.

Those in front go further, under the barrier. The rest follow. As she is walking under the barrier and past it, the first, weary steps on the free forest road, she grasps the arm of the mother walking next to her and, overcome with emotion, she weeps uncontrollably. She raises her wet face toward the face that is bending over her, ashamed because she has entered into freedom with tears...

Is that day? Those streaks there by the horizon, over the cornfields? Is that really day—*their* day?

Have cornfields existed without their knowing it? And flowers along the edge, vague and hesitant in the early daylight? And has all that appeared from the cruel winter, without their noticing that there was a spring and a summer? And that sleepy morning greeting from the birds in the trees along the road—has that been there each morning, even when they were not there to be surprised by the sound of it?

It is not possible—but it *is* day. The streaks of daylight become broader until the light reigns over them all: the fields, the flowers, the trees, the birds, and over the group of tired adults and children whose feet are dragging but whose gazes and voices are greeting all these long-forgotten things in astonishment.

"A house!"

They scarcely know what a house looks like anymore. Barracks—barracks, packed with people—barracks completely at the mercy of the cold of the winter and the sun of the summer—barracks where from outside you heard all the tangle of voices, the loud voices of those dealing out commands or those who were quarreling. But a house? A house, with the shadow of trees around it and the silence of its solitude? Has that survived in the meantime—even here?

Then they point, and with happy, subdued voices they name a lilac—an elderberry—a chestnut tree—a hollyhock—oh, and a laburnum! Like little children unwrapping birthday presents and calling out in surprise, they *must* call out what they see. "And a woman!"

Nothing else has existed to them except star men and star women and star children and uniforms, uniforms with death's heads. And here is a woman under a tree by a house, rinsing out her laundry in a washtub—a woman wearing an apron, with wet, bare arms. Has this existed all that time without their knowing it? "And a church!"

Formerly, long ago, there were villages in Holland that you could already recognize at a distance by their steeples. What was that like? In the wide fields you could search for a point that was familiar to you—a tower that beckoned to you. And here, suddenly, there is a nearby church on a little hill surrounded by trees that give off shadows on the gravestones in the circle. Gravestones—did that still exist, that people could die in houses and be buried underneath their own stone?

"And a store!"

But in front of the closed curtain of the store a sign is hanging which states that there is no one there because the shopkeeper had to go to the front. Such boards are hanging in front of all the closed curtains of stores. No—there are no more stores.

"Oh, and a station!"

Suddenly they understand that this is *their* station, that this is the end of their walking and the beginning of their journey. As they approach it, they see their baggage lying in a heap on the ground, but a train is not there.

They would like to take their smaller bags out of the heap. They recognize these pieces and have packed things for the journey in them, but the barking voice of the man in green reminds them that they are not yet free, not even to have at their disposal what belongs to them, not even to go sit on the ground when their legs no longer want to carry them. They stand there, without support, and no longer dare to hope that a train will ever come to take them away from here.

An open truck comes with the old and the very sick. The sick people are laid on the ground, for the truck must return to the camp. The white faces do not give any hope that they will withstand the long journey—but who can say? Weren't there people who were even more ill, who could not come at all?

Then, slowly and pounding and puffing, the train comes—their train. The children suddenly forget their weariness and scream with excitement. The big girl shivers a little because she believes that she will later step out of this train and see father and mother again. Oh, no...

A group of Sträflinge has come out of the camp and is now forced to assist in the liberation of others, a happiness in which they have no part. They hurl the baggage into the baggage car with coarse jokes from the one to the other and with white, tight-lipped faces.

But the star children climb into the cars and, bewildered, see the broad, soft seats—the luxury of second-class compartments, with mirrors in which for the first time in years they see their own faces. The adults, exhausted, let themselves fall into their seats and feel the long-forgotten virtue of the back of a seat against them. They are too overwhelmed for words or tears.

The little girl who has grown up in dormitories and barracks stands for a moment, looking around in bewilderment. Then she slaps the soft seat with her flat little hand and calls, "Oooo! What pretty mattresses they have in this barrack!"

Passage to Heaven

IT EXISTS, THEN, a train that takes you from hell to heaven.

Once there were trains that brought those star children from heaven to hell—but that was something else; she must not think about that now.

She had previously thought that she would sleep as soon as she sat down—but now outside the window the world is opening for her, passing by in all its beauty. She has no time to sleep now. She must look and not let anything go by unseen. She must breathe in and drink in everything.

Is this the country that has brought a curse over the world, the country that has turned children into star children, driven forth and snatched away? Is this the country that you must learn to hate, the country against which you must pray for revenge to the God who has seen all that sorrow? Then why is it so pretty and sunny and rolling and so far-reaching to where the sky touches it? Can you really hate it and pray for revenge against it when the gleaming world is going past you—and when you are fifteen years old and on your way to father and mother? Oh, no—but this country, this ground, these hills have not done it. It was only the men who walked over the land and who lived on the land—they were the ones who have brought the curse. Now those men themselves are no longer there to walk on and to live on the land, they are no longer there to farm it and to raise food on it. Now those men themselves have moved farther on to bring a curse upon other men and upon themselves. On this land, this beautiful, sunny land, they have set strangers, prisoners, who must farm it and raise food on it for those who remain here and for those who have left. The ground is farmed by hands that sow seeds and hatred—by hands that want to be farming a distant and deserted land, sowing seeds and love.

The train hardly passes by any cities, and it almost never stops. But as it rides slowly for a few moments, there is a group of these prisoners at work, close by the rails. Their shaved heads are not bent over their work but are raised to the train passing by that comes *so* close to them that they can discern the stars on the breasts of the passengers and thus understand who they are.

The girl presses against the window and looks into the thin, gray faces of the prisoners.

They have faces from far away: high cheekbones, behind which the eyes seem to sink away, but not deeply enough to hide the fierce and dangerous burning in them. One holds her gaze, and when he sees that she is listening with her eyes, he makes two motions. First, his one hand goes along his throat with a cutting gesture, and then his two hands break something invisible *so* vehemently that it seems that she hears something crack.

She has understood. She is shocked that she has understood. She has understood that those responsible for bringing such misery upon him and all the others should have their throats cut, should be cracked in two. Oh, God, she has understood. She nods slowly and seriously. The prisoner nods back because he knows that his gesture has been understood.

Her heart is beating wildly. Shouldn't he have seen that she is just fifteen and therefore cannot understand *such* unbridled hatred? But she has understood that hatred—that is the most terrible part about it. Suddenly she is not fifteen anymore, but infinitely old and infinitely tired.

She goes away from the window and, small and defeated, she crawls back to her seat. She wants only to go to sleep now. She does not want to think anymore about that face with the sunken, burning eyes, or that cutting hand, or those two cracking fists. The train is now well past him. She wants to think about father and mother whom she will see again. When? She is riding to them. Now she is sure that she is on her way to them. She will write a letter to them as soon as she is free and can drop a letter into a mailbox. How long has it been since she was able to put a letter in a mailbox? How long will it be before she can do that? Perhaps before that happens she will be with father and mother in Palestine. And she has no money to buy a postage stamp. What would she write? "Dearest father and mother, I am free." And what else? I am free—I am free—I am free—I am free...

Listen: the train is saying it, too: I am free—I am free—I am free—I am free...

But the fists of the prisoner break the word in two, and it cracks...

She awakens with a start and immediately goes back to sleep again.

When it is evening she sees the red sun going down behind mountains surrounding a clear river that is still narrow and near its source. They say that it is the Danube.

The Danube? But...but they are out of this country, then...Can that be true?

"Not yet," the grown-ups smile. "But almost."

Then is it true that they are on their way to Palestine? If they are almost out of this country now?

"It's true," nod the adults. They believe it themselves now.

The darkness of night may come now, and she can become as tired as she wishes, for it does not matter at all. The train is bringing her farther on, to another country, and although it is ruled by this land, it is nevertheless a different country., During the night, the train will bring her closer to father and mother. She would not mind if she had to travel for weeks and weeks, without being able to lie down and really sleep. She would not mind going hungry if all their provisions for the journey were eaten, as long as she is brought closer to father and mother.

The Danube...and this morning they were still walking in rows of five...And last night they were going under the barrier...

When morning comes and, dusty and stiff, she awakens from the last of the countless short sleeps, the Danube has broadened, and they have stopped at the outside edge of Vienna. No one knows whether or not they will get off here and have a meal somewhere; they still have bread and margarine left over, thus they could continue to travel without a rest stop—but oh, a *little* bit of refreshment...

Then the train jerks again and brings them a little farther, again a little farther, until they see the door opening wide at a large station and hear that they may get off. Getting off at a station in a big city, not in a camp!

Buses with real seats bring them through sad, damaged neighborhoods. They stop in front of a tall building that is a home for the homeless. There are a few groups that have already been dropped off earlier by the bus, and the children from those groups have already been inside and upstairs. Now they stand with excited faces, waiting and all calling out at once, even before the later groups can understand them.

"There are beds with sheets! Single beds, without anyone above you!"

"That *can't* be!"

"Honest! And warm water out of the tap!"

"Really?"

"Really! And we get hot food here, they've said, as much as we want!"

Now, they would have thought that, to eat as much as they wanted. But a bed with a sheet, and warm water for washing—oh, if only that were true!

"And," nods a little boy intensely, to outdo the others, "and when you go from one barrack to the other, you have to climb up a *stairway!* A *high* stairway! And I am *not* afraid of the stairs."

It is all true—even eating as much hot food as you want. For when she finishes her mug of delicious soup and her deep platter of vegetables, she may go back to where those women are serving the meal quietly and without shouting, and she may ask them for more. But she cannot eat a second helping, for this is more than she has eaten in a long time. Tomorrow, perhaps, if they are still here.

There is even more that is true: the trucks have taken their baggage from the train, and everything is displayed there on the pavement in front of the building, so that all they need to do is look for their pieces. She finds almost all of her own things, and what she does not find does not matter to her because she feels much too rich and happy already. She washes herself completely and goes to lie down in her bed with a sheet, without anyone above her, and in the middle of the day. Her friend lies in the bed next to her, and they look at each other and laugh in disbelief before falling asleep.

But the old woman in the bed on the other side of her sits erect, her hands in front of her face and in a complaining voice she cries, "That they have done *that* to us! That they have done *that* to us!" Disheartened, the girls listen but do not understand her. Then they pull the covers over their ears and go to sleep.

They walk freely through the entire building. Little children are cuddled by dark brown men who are also guests in this house and are on their way back to their own country. They have lots of cigarettes and sweets with them because they were prisoners of war and received many packages. They give cigarettes to the adults, and they stuff the children full of biscuits and chocolate until they are sick to their stomachs, for they are not used to so much and such rich food. Those men pat the children on their cheeks and smile broadly at their delight.

It is all unbelievable, like a fairy tale.

But from the courtyard comes the sound of many people and of voices barking commands. When one of the boys climbs into the high window sill of the ground floor, he sees a heap of men, women, and children thrown together, with a few men in uniforms among them. The boy knows what is happening, for it is the same as when he himself was taken from his house during a roundup and thrown together with all the others in a heap on the square. Horrified, he lets himself down.

Others go around quickly through the building and ask each person if he has bread left over to give to these people for their journey farther on. They are Hungarian Jews who have been taken away and will now be deported, just as they themselves, who are now liberated, had for years been taken away and deported. And those who yesterday—no, the day before yesterday—those who were hungry and considered a slice of bread a gift can now give away half a loaf and still have enough bread left over.

"I want to give it to them!" calls the girl, with long-forgotten excitement, wanting to climb and take aim. "I can climb onto that window sill!"

She sets herself on her friend's shoulder and a little later is sitting in the niche, looking down on the picture that she has never before seen as a picture because she had been a part of it.

She shivers and breathes deeply. She reaches her arm down to take the bread that her friend passes to her from below. Again and again she aims a piece of bread at the courtyard, where eager arms reach out and where tired, dull eyes become alive with desire to catch it. Her arms work like a machine: grasp the bread on the one side, throw the bread on the other side. Her thoughts are not working at all—they do not want to work.

Then the men in uniform come to the other side of the window and with threats drive the people away to the other corner of the courtyard. They look at her where she is sitting up high, and some of them shake their heads unhappily.

From inside her friend passes her more bread, but her hands fall idly at her side, and she shakes her head just as she has seen the people in the courtyard do. She beckons her friend for her shoulder and silently lets herself slide down.

She cannot contain her dismay—her dismay of what for her has ended and what for these people in the courtyard of her fairy-tale palace, has begun...

It lasts for one day and one night, eating until you have had enough, washing with warm water, sleeping in a bed with a sheet and with no one above you. Then they move on: in buses to the train, which has even softer seats and even broader mirrors than the previous one.

It is difficult for everyone to find a seat, but she takes care that she remains with the father and mother of her friend. As long as she has not yet found her own father and mother...

The Danube becomes wider, and the land becomes prettier—even prettier. Now they know for sure that they are going to Palestine.

And then, when they have just become used to this new little room riding along and have settled into their seats, young girls from their own group go past the doors of all the compartments and call out, "Get ready to go to the dining car!"

Is this a joke? But yesterday's events were not a joke, either...

"Should we bring our food bowl with us?" asks the mother.

The young girl, already a door farther, quickly calls back, "Did you used to bring a food bowl with you when you went out to eat?"

What used to be—come now, who speaks of what used to be...

They look into the mirror and comb their hair before leaving to go to the dining car. On the way each person is stopped by one of the leaders of their group.

"Take off your stars!"

That means...And this is not a joke, either?

The girl pulls wildly at her star; with two hands she breaks the thread that had sewn the star on long ago. She pulls the thread out and stands still with the Jewish star in her hand, the star that had become so much a part of her that she could not even think of herself without it.

But the stream of people is going forward to the dining car, with everyone tearing and pulling on the threads of their stars. She cannot stand still, she must go along, too.

At the entrance to the dining car each person waits a moment, motionless, before going inside. There is a plate, a spoon, a fork, a knife, and a paper napkin set for each one. There are waiters going around among the tables. They are expected, just like rich people on a holiday trip—and no one has money.

The girl sits at a table for four and looks silently and with disbelief into the faces of the other three. All of them are wearing a bewildered smile, and when she looks at the people at the other tables, she sees that same silence and that same smile.

But this is...but surely this is a dream?

She feels the tears stinging in her eyes and is ashamed.

"Don't you put on any airs!" she thinks. "Don't cry now—please don't! Take your handkerchief out and dry your eyes and that's the end of it!"

She grasps in her bag and dries her eyes. Then in dismay she looks at the damp little wad in her hand.

It is her star.

And so the story of the star children is over. They are no longer star children, then, but Jewish children on their way to their own land and to freedom.

And they lived long and happily—a handful of star children chosen by chance from the crowds, the crowds, the crowds of star children who did not live long and happily, whose stars were torn off by God Himself and placed among the other stars in the heavens, as eternal evidence.

Photographs

Star children at school, Roerstraat. From a family album in the collection of the Rijksinstituut voor Oorlogsdocumentatie–Netherlands State Institute for War Documentation, Amsterdam.

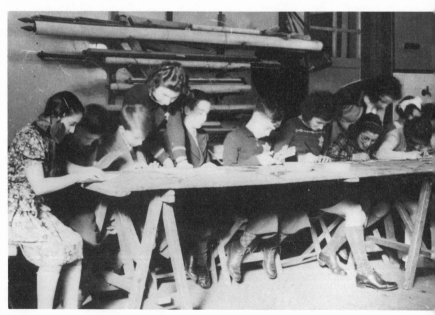

At school, Jan van Eyckstraat.

At school, Tilanusstraat.

Roundup. Empty vans waiting, Waterlooplein, 1941.

Star House. The Joodse Schouwburg as it
appeared after the war.

The Jewish children's home opposite Star House.

On the way to Westerbork.

Deportation, Amsterdam.

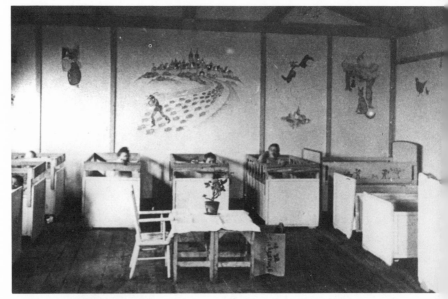

Children's ward, hospital, Westerbork.

Making toys, Westerbork.

Camp orchestra, Westerbork.

Dancing the hora, Westerbork.

Westerbork.

Westerbork.

Westerbork.

Freight cars leaving Westerbork.

Star children, Bergen-Belsen, April 1945. (British official photograph.)

The author and one of her star children, Westerbork.

Terese Edelstein received the B.A. and M.A.T. degrees from Washington University. A teacher of violin at Detroit Community Music School, she has also taught in St. Louis, Missouri, and in Durham and Chapel Hill, North Carolina.

Inez Smidt is a physician in Leiden.

Harry James Cargas, of Webster University, is Associate Editor of the journal *Holocaust and Genocide Studies* and a member of the United States Holocaust Memorial Council. He has written widely on the Christian response to the Holocaust.

The manuscript was edited by Catherine Thatcher. The book was designed by Joanne Kinney. The typeface for the text and the display is Trump Mediaeval. The book is printed on 60-lb. Booktext and is bound in Joanna Western Mills Devon cloth over binder's boards.

Manufactured in the United States of America.